MINES OF CORNWALL AND DEVON
AN HISTORIC PHOTOGRAPHIC RECORD

PETER STANIER

MENEDRESS
Ha
11/7/1998

TWELVEHEADS PRESS

TRURO • 1998

CONTENTS

TWELVEHEADS PRESS

First published 1998 by Twelveheads Press,
Chy Mengleth, Twelveheads, Truro, Cornwall TR4 8SN.

ISBN 0 906294 401
British Library Cataloguing-in-Publication Data.
A catalogue record for this book is available from the British Library.

Designed by Alan Kittridge
Printed by The Amadeus Press Ltd., Huddersfield, Yorks.

INTRODUCTION

THE BRITISH GEOLOGICAL SURVEY possesses a large and important collection of photographs taken over the years since the early 1900s, showing geological and related landscape features throughout Britain. A number of these include mines and quarries, where certain mineral deposits and formations are exposed. Inevitably, the photographers also took views of the miners and their methods, with pumping and winding engines, dressing floors and other equipment. Some photographs from this great store were selected to illustrate the 'economic geology' sections of the Survey's various Sheet Memoirs and Regional Geologies, but the others have not appeared in print before. These are now records of great interest, especially to local historians, industrial archaeologists, industrial railway historians and economic geologists. The collection also shows the technological advances made in photography, from large glass plates to film negatives.

This book is intended as a companion volume to the author's *Quarries of England and Wales* (1995), which covers quarries across a wide geographical area, but in this case photographs of mining outside South-West England are mostly absent from the BGS collection. The book is therefore restricted to the important mining counties of Cornwall and Devon. It has been divided into convenient subjects to illustrate the techniques of mineral extraction during the first half of the twentieth century, although it is seen that some processes inevitably overlap between chapters.

The historic photographs reproduced here were taken by four men in two distinct time periods: 1903-7, and 1945. They range in location from the wild Atlantic cliffs of the far west to the more sheltered eastern flanks of Dartmoor. Some mines are given more prominence than others because the Survey's collection is itself selective. Most concern tin mining and streaming in Cornwall, although wolfram and iron are also represented. Devon is less prominent in the collection, but it does include the large wolfram workings at Hemerdon and, in contrast to all else, micaceous haematite, barytes and ball clay mining.

Although a number of the photographs have been published before, this was many years ago, in the Survey's own early Cornwall and Devon *Memoirs* beginning in 1906, the *South-West England Regional Geology*, 1935 (2nd ed. 1948) and *The Metalliferous Mining Region of South-West England* in 1956. Some have appeared more recently in books of mining photographs, but in most cases their true origin and dates were not fully acknowledged. Now for the first time many of these photographs have been brought together with full accompanying details such as times, dates, orientation, grid references and the photographers' names. The fixing of a photograph at a precise moment in time is specially important in the case of dressing processes which were being continuously modified and changed. Reference is also made in the text to the location of other published photographs, as an aid to interpreting the industrial archaeology of the sites.

CHAPTER ONE
THE PHOTOGRAPHIC COLLECTION

DURING THE PERIOD COVERED by this book (1903-45), the Geological Survey of Great Britain was first based at the Museum of Practical Geological in Jermyn Street, Piccadilly, London, before these two bodies moved to Exhibition Road, South Kensington, in 1935. They were later incorporated into the Institute of Geological Sciences, which in turn became the British Geological Survey in 1984, with a new headquarters at Keyworth near Nottingham. The museum remains in London, where it has been transformed into the Earth Galleries of the Natural History Museum.

THE GEOLOGICAL SURVEY IN CORNWALL AND DEVON

The Geological Survey was active in the South West since the early nineteenth century and it is significant that this important region was the subject of the Survey's first published Memoir (De La Beche, 1839). This covered the geology, with additional information on mines and minerals, but the Survey did not return to the complexities of mineral deposits and mining in the region for another 60 years. In 1899-1913, detailed re-mapping of most of Cornwall and south Devon was carried out under the direction of Clement Reid, the District Geologist. During the period of the early photographs in this book, he was accompanied in the field by other geologists such as George Barrow, J. B. Hill, D. A. MacAlister and W. A. E. Ussher. J. B. Scrivenor was present in 1903, and the party

was joined three years later by Henry Dewey and the petrographer Dr John S. Flett. The latter worked on the petrographic study of igneous and metamorphic rocks and ore deposits, while MacAlister examined the mining aspects. The results of this work were published in a series of Sheet Memoirs, many of which contain a section or appendix on mining.

In the Great War, the Survey paid attention to certain strategic minerals, which led to the publication of a series of 'Special Reports on the Mineral Resources of Great Britain' (e.g. Dewey and Dines, 1923). Although nationwide, it was natural that these should include the South West region. There was a revival of interest when H. G. Dines began a detailed study of mining geology from 1938 and worked on it throughout the 1940s. The result was the publication in 1956 of *The Metalliferous Mining Region of South West England*. Although now over 40 years old, no mining historian should ignore reference to this standard two-volumed work.

PHOTOGRAPHY AT THE SURVEY

Geological assistants employed by the old Survey were also photographers, and from the early twentieth century they travelled the country extensively, recording rock exposures, landforms and other geological features. Economic geology - mines, pits and quarries - represents an inevitable portion of

their photographs. A separate photographic unit was later established, and the library of the British Geological Survey now houses a large and unrivalled archive of photographs. Those selected for this book come from the 'A' series of England and Wales, which contains over 14,500 negatives and is still being enlarged. Other series include, for example, the parallel 'B' and 'C' series covering Scotland. A1, the first registered photograph, is dated 21 May 1904. However, the earliest field photograph in the series would appear to be A84, which shows tin mine workings at Cligga Head in Cornwall, and was one of several taken by J. B. Scrivenor in the St Agnes district in June 1903. This, and two others, are illustrated in this book.

THE PHOTOGRAPHERS

The four photographers with whom this book is concerned are T. C. Hall, D. A. MacAlister, and J. B. Scrivenor in 1903-7, and Jack Rhodes in 1945.

Thomas Clifford Fitzwilliam Hall (1883-1956), having studied at the Royal School of Mines, was employed from May 1903 as an assistant, working in the Petrographical Department with John S. Flett who was to contribute to the Survey's Memoirs in Cornwall and on Dartmoor then in preparation. Hall became responsible for photography in the Survey's English division, and a number of his photographs were taken in Cornwall and Devon, where he went to help the geologists in the field. Beginning with a series around Falmouth, his earliest was taken on 8 August 1904 of Sunny Cove (A6), and published in Hill and MacAlister, 1906, Plate VIII. It appears that he worked closely with MacAlister in the same year and no doubt supervised the taking of the latter's photographs, while taking many himself. In 1906, Hall was at Botallack and Levant in the Land's End district, moving to mid-Cornwall and Bodmin Moor in the next year. He left the Survey in September 1910, when he was appointed lecturer at the Camborne School of Metalliferous Mining in Cornwall,

and his subsequent distinguished career as an economic geologist took him all over the world.

Hall was accompanied in Cornwall by **Donald Alexander MacAlister** (1875-1968), who was responsible for sections on mining geology in the Memoirs, most notably in those covering the Falmouth and Truro and the Land's End sheets (Hill and MacAlister, 1906; Reid and Flett, 1907). MacAlister contributed to three other Memoirs, and was joint author of three more. He had joined the Survey as a 'Temporary Geologist' in 1902 and was a 'Mining Geologist' by 1905. After working around the Camborne and Redruth mines he moved eastwards, first to the St Austell area. MacAlister tried his hand at some photographs, but neither he nor Hall have been positively identified in the photographs; it is very likely that one or the other appears in the views of dressing floors (Chapter Six) and both together with a group of miners at South Crofty (Chapter Five).

John Brooke Scrivenor (1876-1950) worked for the Survey as a geologist in 1902-5, and was joint author for the Newquay sheet Memoir (Reid and Scrivenor, 1906). He took the earliest photographs in the whole collection in 1903, when he was examining the Perranporth and St Agnes areas. Two years later, he resigned to take up an appointment as geologist to the Federated Malay States Government. After his return to England, he was active in Cornwall and Devon as late as the 1940s, when papers were published in the *Geological Magazine* in 1948-49.

There is a break in the photography of 38 years, from 1907 to 1945. All the 1945 photographs were taken by **John (Jack) Rhodes**. He had joined his father (also John) at the Survey as a General Assistant in 1910, although his career was soon interrupted by the Great War when he served as an air mechanic in the Royal Naval Air Service from 1916 to 1919. Within a year of his appointment, he was engaged in photographic work, replacing Hall by printing plates at the Survey for Flett as well as taking to the field. Rhodes travelled

Registered Number.	GEOLOGICAL SURVEY AND MUSEUM.	Photographer's Number.
41.	BRITISH PHOTOGRAPHS.	44.T.CH.

Photographed by	W.A. MacAlister + T.C.Hall.			

Locality	Wheal Grenville, Camborne.	County	Maps	Latitude
		Cornwall.	1 in.	6 in.	50° 12′ 5″
			352	Longitude 5° 16′ 40″

SUBJECT OF PHOTOGRAPH

Cornish Stamps.

Direction of View	Size of Objects in Foreground	Plate	Lens and stop
looking. W.	indicated by figure	Imp. Spec. Rapid.	Cooke 4·4. F.16.

Date	Time	Light	Exposure (and Screen)	Destination (For use in Office only)
25. Sept. 1904.	12. 45. p.m.	Bright Sunshine	1/8. second.	A 1.

widely on photographic assignments throughout England and Wales during his long career with the Survey (Stanier, 1995, 4). One of his last major assignments was to the South West and it is from these plates that the illustrations for this book have been chosen. They have added interest, being at a landmark date at the very end of the Second World War (the war in Europe had been over since May but still lingered on in the Far East until mid-August). Perhaps the last of his published photographs was taken in 1949 at the Great Weldon stone quarry, Northamptonshire. Jack Rhodes retired from the Survey in 1956.

The early photographers used a half-plate wooden field camera and tripod together with glass plate negatives for all their pictures. The photographs were usually recorded in meticulous detail - the location being indicated by latitude and longitude in degrees, minutes and seconds (the metric National Grid reference system did not come into operation until after 1945), the date, time of day, weather conditions,

Cornish stamps engine at Wheal Grenville

A 24-inch rotative beam engine of 1864 is seen with two flywheels and driving 84 heads of Cornish stamps. In front of the stamps the 'pulp' is concentrated on floors with round buddles - convex (left) and concave (right foreground). Looking west, the distant building is the mortuary chapel for a cemetery, which still survives. The site of the old stamps has completely gone, although the New Stamps engine house, installed in 1891 for a second set of 96 stamps, still stands nearby at SW 666386. Wheal Grenville was near the west end of a long run of mines sunk on the Great Flat Lode just south of Camborne. In 1906, the mine joined with South Condurrow to become Grenville United Mines, then 355 fathoms (649 metres) deep. Work ceased in 1920. This photograph was published with no date, in Trounson, 1980, Plate 8.

D. A. MacAlister and T. C. Hall, 12.45 p.m. 25 September 1904 [A41] SW 662387

camera orientation, lens, plates and exposure time. Brief explanatory notes usually accompany each photograph in the collection's albums. The example illustrated here is by MacAlister and Hall, and shows the notes accompanying the photograph of the Wheal Grenville stamps, in September 1904. The Photographer's Number '44. T.C.H.' (top right) seems to indicate that Hall was in charge, even though both men are credited with the photograph. The same occurs, for example, with the photographs of dressing floors at Dolcoath and South Crofty; underground at Dolcoath (A60) is both but East Pool (A61) is MacAlister alone.

Records of the later, 1945, photographs are less detailed. Jack Rhodes was now using a field camera on a tripod using Kodak panchromatic half-plate negative film ($6\frac{1}{2}$" x $4\frac{3}{4}$"). He had continued to use glass negatives until at least 23 March 1937 (photograph A7078).

PHOTOGRAPHERS AT WORK

The early photographers were said to have travelled on occasion on horseback or bicycle, and the carrying of their heavy equipment must have been no small problem. Hall sometimes used a bicycle, this being seen in at least one of his plates. In 1945, Rhodes had the use of a motor car. This was good fortune for he had an extremely busy period in August that year, travelling between mines in the far west of Cornwall and the ball clay pits of Bovey Tracey in Devon. The volume of work he got through says much for improved mobility brought by the car (few mining sites were readily accessible by public transport) and the less cumbersome photographic equipment then in use.

Where precise times are given with the earlier photographs, and where there are several pictures at the same site, one can almost see the photographer scrambling about choosing a new viewpoint. For example, between 2.30 p.m. and 5.00 p.m. on the afternoon of 24 September 1904, Hall and MacAlister were busy photographing the dressing floors at Dolcoath and South Crofty, with plates taken at five to 15 minute intervals (see A39 to A52). There is, however, a discrepancy on the following day, when Wheal Grenville (A42) and the view from Dolcoath (A37) are both given the time of 1.00 p.m., yet they are over a mile apart!

The photographs' contribution to the study of industrial archaeology is their record of mine buildings and equipment that have been demolished long since. Comparison with other contemporary photographs is informative, especially that of the classic Camborne mining landscape (A37), where even the space of 11 years since the photograph taken by Burrow and Thomas (1893) shows there has been some demolition, addition or modification of buildings and shafts.

OTHER PHOTOGRAPHIC RECORDS

Cornish mining has been particularly well documented on film, and there are important photographic collections, such as that held by the Royal Institution of Cornwall in Truro. One of the finest underground mining photographers was John Charles Burrow, who took a number of superb glass-plates after 1891, encouraged by William Thomas, a lecturer at the Camborne Mining School. Several were published as sepia plates, with additional notes by Thomas, in 'Mongst Mines and Miners (1893), for which Burrow gained the first Mining Fellowship of the Royal Photographic Society. These classic scenes in Dolcoath, East Pool, Cook's Kitchen and Blue Hills mines have been reproduced, deservedly, in many subsequent publications. Other books containing large numbers of historic photographs include, for example, works by D. B. Barton (1967a and 1967b) and J. H. Trounson (1968, 1980 and 1981). An original photographer, Geoffrey Ordish had the foresight to make a systematic record of Cornish mines at a later date when they had been abandoned, from the 1930s to 1960s (Ordish, 1967 and 1968). It is only now that we can appreciate what has been lost.

CHAPTER TWO
MINING IN CORNWALL AND DEVON

MINERALS AND MINING

THE GEOLOGY, MINERALS AND MINING history of the South West have probably received more attention in the literature than any other region in Britain, and for a more detailed picture the reader is encouraged to follow up the selected bibliography given at the end of this book. The mineral wealth of Cornwall and Devon is closely related to the granite bosses which were intruded beneath older Devonian mudstones and slates about 280 million years ago. Subsequent erosion has revealed them at the surface to form the moorland spine of the South West peninsula from Land's End to Dartmoor. Around each granite margin is the metamorphic aureole, a ring of baked rocks known locally as killas, and it is here that the richest mining districts are found.

The mineral lodes were created when mineralising vapours and fluids passed up from below and crystallised in fissures which had opened in the cooling and hardening granite. According to their depth and temperatures at which they were formed, they contain tin, copper, wolfram, arsenic, zinc, lead and iron, along with unwanted 'gangue' minerals such as tourmaline, quartz, fluorspar and calcite. The tin and copper lodes extend from the granite into the killas and trend, generally, east-west. Lead, zinc and iron were deposited at a late stage in mainly north-south lodes (cross-courses) which are found further away from the granite. The lodes are usually steeply inclined or near-vertical, but may dip at a lesser angle (the Great Flat Lode south of Camborne lies at 40°). They may also be displaced by faulting. A 'stockwork' is where thin veins occur in a mass.

Inevitably, the mining photographs in this book are dominated by TIN, the metal for which Cornwall is especially well known. The ore is cassiterite, or tin oxide, a dark black-brown mineral. After treatment and concentration, 'black tin' might be about 60-70 per cent pure tin metal. While once more important than tin mines, the mining of copper ores had collapsed and was insignificant by the time of the photographs. WOLFRAM, a tungstate of iron and manganese, is the ore for tungsten and is usually found with tin. It was once discarded as a nuisance until it became of strategic value. Iron ore is widespread in both Cornwall and Devon, but has only been worked commercially at certain places. The two types seen in this book are HAEMATITE and the variety MICACEOUS HAEMATITE. A non-metalliferous mineral, BARYTES, was also formed in lodes and is often associated with galena (lead). This heavy spar, or barium sulphate, was formerly thrown to waste but is seen being mined here in its own right. In contrast with all these minerals, the BALL CLAY mined in Devon is completely different, being of sedimentary origin and deposited in deep basins at Bovey Tracey in the south and Petrockstow in the north.

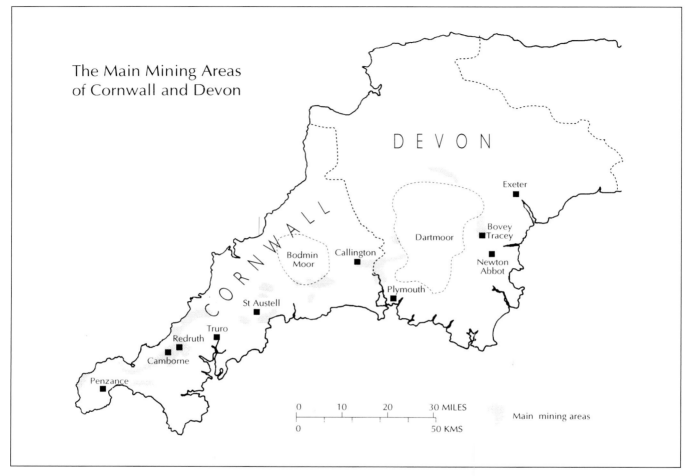

The Main Mining Areas
of Cornwall and Devon

DEVON

Exeter

Bovey
Tracey

Dartmoor

Newton
Abbot

Bodmin
Moor

Callington

CORNWALL

Plymouth

St Austell

Truro

Redruth

Camborne

Penzance

| 0 | 10 | 20 | 30 MILES |

0   50 KMS

Main mining areas

The earliest workings for tin were in streamworks. Past erosion of lodes had removed tin stones (cassiterite), sorted and deposited them in valley gravels where they could be won relatively easily by washing away the lighter material. As methods improved over the centuries, increasingly poorer deposits could be worked, so many valley floors have been turned over time and time again, often destroying earlier evidence.

Streamworks were still abundant in medieval times, although there were now shallow underground workings along some lodes. The 'black tin' produced was smelted in small water-powered 'blowing houses'. Dartmoor was for a while the greatest tin producer in Europe, but when the easier streams became worked out Cornwall regained its pre-eminence. The tin industries of Cornwall and Devon were regulated by the ancient Stannaries which held jurisdiction

10

over large areas, with courts and a parliament. 'Coinage' took place at Stannary Towns, where each tin ingot was weighed to assess the duty to be paid to the Duke of Cornwall and a corner, or coign, was struck off to be assayed for quality. The tin block had to be stamped with the Duchy seal before it could be sold. Coinage ceased in 1838 and the courts in 1896.

Drainage was the main obstacle to deep mining for tin and copper, a problem not satisfactorily overcome until the invention of the steam pumping engine, first the beam engines of Newcomen and Watt in the eighteenth century, followed by developments and refinements by famous Cornish engineers such as Richard Trevithick, Arthur Woolf and many others. The Cornish beam engine reached perfection in the nineteenth century, first for pumping and then for winding and ore crushing (stamping). Many of these advances were made on the copper mines which overshadowed tin until the second half of the nineteenth century. Dolcoath Mine at Camborne, for example, was first successfully worked for copper, but when that started to fail in the 1840s the mine was able to turn to deep tin - a good fortune enjoyed at many other mines. Dolcoath became the greatest tin producer by the end of the nineteenth century and was to reach 550 fathoms (1006 metres), the deepest of any mine in Cornwall. It closed in 1921 after a century of continuous working. Having started in copper, Camborne-Redruth became the major tin mining district, but others were around Callington, St Just and St Agnes.

Because of the quantities of fuel required for smelting, most copper ores were shipped to South Wales, from which coal was brought back in return for the engines on the mines. Tin, however, was smelted at home on a larger scale as the industry expanded, in smelting houses set up in the eighteenth and nineteenth centuries with reverberatory furnaces to produce 'white tin'. The main centres were Truro, Redruth and Penzance, and tin blocks were shipped from ports such as Truro and Penzance. Uses of tin in the nineteenth century included bronze, solder, pewter and tin plate. As well as smelting, other associated industries to develop alongside mining included engineering, explosives and fuse works.

The history of mining is one of faith and perseverance with occasional compensating riches on the one side, and

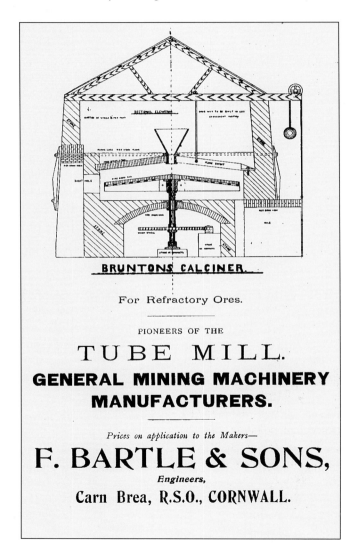

BRUNTONS CALCINER.

For Refractory Ores.

PIONEERS OF THE

TUBE MILL.

GENERAL MINING MACHINERY MANUFACTURERS.

Prices on application to the Makers—

F. BARTLE & SONS,

Engineers,

Carn Brea, R.S.O., CORNWALL.

disastrous financial losses and hardship on the other. Mining has always been a risky business, subject to fluctuations in metal prices. The nineteenth century saw prices tumble with the discovery and development of foreign ore bodies, and the result was disaster for home metal mining. Following close on the rapid collapse of its copper mining industry, Cornwall's tin mines suffered setback after setback as the price fell from the 1860s, due first to the American Civil War. There was one brief, heady boom for a few years when tin prices rose to £153 per ton in 1872, and in the previous year Cornish tin mines had yielded their greatest ever - 16,272 tons of black tin, or 10,900 tons of metallic tin. The fate of tin mining was sealed after 1873 when then discovery of tin in Australia coincided with renewed output from Malayan alluvial workings, and tin prices fell rapidly. After some recovery came a major depression with tin prices falling as low as £64 per ton in 1896 (£34 for black tin) which few mines could survive for long. Bolivian tin entered the market at the turn of the century. Many important mines, including Botallack, closed in the 1890s, so that by the 1900s - the time of the first BGS photographs - this disaster had left only a handful of mines at work.

TWENTIETH-CENTURY MINING AND THE PHOTOGRAPHS

This book records mining practices in the first half of the twentieth century, between 1903 and 1945, a period which witnessed many changes in the industry. The first photographs, in 1903-7, show the mining industry at a point where it was struggling on from the severe depression of the 1890s. Ever hopeful, there had been some investment to improve tin dressing, such as the introduction of modern Frue vanners at Dolcoath and South Crofty.

Tin prices were steadily recovering - to around £140 by 1905 - which encouraged a revival of mining and exploration over the next few years. Tin mining was by now confined to Cornwall, where fresh activity was seen throughout the county in the years up to the Great War. As a measure of the confidence still felt in Cornish mining, Grenville United Mines was formed in 1906 and Geevor Tin Mines Ltd. in 1911. Even parts of the old Botallack Mine were reopened. Prices rose in the Great War, by the end of which there were eight large tin mines left in Cornwall: East Pool & Agar, Dolcoath, South Crofty, Grenville United, Geevor, Tincroft, Tresavean and Levant. Together these employed 3,471 men and produced 4,525 tons in 1918 (Barton, 1967a, 256).

This period had also witnessed an increasing interest in wolfram, an accessory mineral usually found with tin and which was once discarded. It found little use until tungsten alloys were developed for high-speed steels in the second half of the nineteenth century; by 1910, tungsten filaments in electric lamps were almost universal. Wolfram was being exploited in streamworks at Buttern Hill on Bodmin Moor and as a by-product at some surviving tin mines. It became strategically important during the Great War, and Cornwall's production rose from 180 tons in 1913 to 347 tons in 1916. New developments were undertaken, rather unsuccessfully, at Hemerdon on the edge of Dartmoor, while wartime prospecting resulted in a completely new wolfram venture at Castle-an-Dinas. This mine was begun in 1916 and worked for another 41 years.

After the Great War, the story is of occasional periods of optimism in the face of continued decline. 1919 saw the Levant man-engine tragedy which left 31 miners dead and many others injured. Then came a severe slump when tin prices crashed throughout 1920 from as high as £396 down to £156 in March 1921, a month when only the Giew Mine near St Ives was still in production. 1921 was a disastrous year for the Camborne mines, with the closure of Dolcoath and the temporary closure of East Pool & Agar brought about by a collapse of ground. The resulting rise in water underground threatened neighbouring South Crofty, where a 90-inch pumping engine was hurriedly installed at New Cook's Kitchen Shaft. Only 370 tons of tin were produced in Cornwall in 1922, but as prices picked up again after this low point there was some renewed activity, including a revitalised Dolcoath (1923-30), Wheal Kitty at St Agnes (1925-30), exploration at Polhigey (1926-30) and Wheal Reeth (1927). A notable failure, though, was the new 2,000-foot (610 metres) Tolgus Shaft which was abandoned in 1928 after five years' work. The new Taylor's Shaft at East Pool & Agar of 1922-4 was a greater success which allowed for the re-opening and continuation of that mine until 1945.

Yet another depression in 1930 brought the closure of these ventures along with Levant, so that only East Pool and Geevor were left at work. The following year was also significant for the closure of the Cornish Tin Smelting Co.'s works at Seleggan near Redruth, the last tin smelting works in the county. South Crofty had kept its pumps going so was able to re-open in 1931; the mine acquired the setts of Dolcoath and Roskear four years later. By the middle of the decade Porkellis, Wheal Reeth, Wheal Breage and Great Work were active in the Helston area, and Wheal Kitty at St Agnes restarted in 1937. Throughout this time Geevor had continued to work on with good results. Some lesser mines were also active, employing a handful of men, and Mulberry, Wheal Prosper and Treveddoe are examples illustrated in this book.

Mining was not confined to tin during these inter-war years. In the Teign Valley lead mining district on the east side of Dartmoor, barytes had been mined at Bridford increasingly from the last quarter of the nineteenth century when markets opened up in the chemical industries. Bridford Mine was worked vigorously and efficiently by outside interests since 1927. Laporte Minerals Ltd. became involved and there were developments at the surface and below ground. In the same area, micaceous haematite was exploited at Great Rock Mine by the Ferrubron Manufacturing Co., who had been here since 1902. The ore was crushed and dressed, and used in its unsmelted form for making anti-corrosive paints. In Cornwall, an experiment at opencast working the Great Perran Iron Lode at Treamble in the 1930s was not fully successful.

Tin (and wolfram) became especially important during the Second World War after Malaya was lost in 1941. The Cornish Tin Mining Advisory Committee oversaw a wartime programme of trials and prospecting in 1942-44, but none of these led to any significant rise in output. Near Plymouth, the Hemerdon wolfram mine was re-activated with much investment, but to little avail.

The 1945 photographs taken by Rhodes are significant because they show the condition of Cornish tin mining in the middle of the twentieth century just before new investment and modernisation would bring changes at the surviving mines during the next 50 years. East Pool had been struggling in the 1930s and was in fact only saved by rising tin prices as war approached again. The mine survived by means of a government subsidy in 1941-45, but by 1945 wartime working conditions and labour shortages had left their mark. Losses were incurred and the ailing mine closed. A receiver was appointed in 1947 and the equipment sold off. Thus ended the life of Cornwall's second greatest tin mine after 138 years, although Taylor's pumping engine was kept at work to drain South Crofty.

Micaceous haematite and barytes were still being mined on eastern Dartmoor in 1945. Other underground workings in Devon at this time were of an entirely different nature and therefore of interest. These were the ball clay deposits of the Bovey Basin and Petrockstow, the former also being photographed by Rhodes.

END PIECE

It is now just over half a century since the date of the last photographs. It is a period which has seen the familiar story of closures, a great resurgence and depression again. In the 1950s, the last of the Cornish pumping engines were stopped and replaced by electric pumps at South Crofty and East Pool. The wolfram mine at Castle-an-Dinas continued until 1957. In

Wheal Concorde
The short-lived Wheal Concorde, near Blackwater, a victim of the collapse of the tin market.

Devon, the Bridford barytes mine closed in 1958, with the Great Rock micaceous haematite mine continuing until 1969. The only mines left at work in Devon today are underground drifts extracting ball clay from the Bovey Beds of the Teign valley.

The greatest activity was in Cornish tin mining. South Crofty and Geevor were the only survivors until the 1960s when rising world tin prices encouraged new developments, with exploratory diamond drilling all over the county and new mines opening in the west at Wheal Jane, Mount Wellington, Pendarves and Wheal Concorde. Much was also invested in developments at South Crofty and Geevor, the latter extending its workings into the old Levant mine and towards Botallack. However, neither a proposed new mine at Redmoor nor the Hemerdon opencast wolfram mine were to reach fruition. The artificially high price of tin reached over £10,000 per tonne before falling in the international tin market collapse in October 1985. Prices fell to around £3,000 before steadying, and casualties were inevitable. Geevor and Wheal Jane struggled on for a while, but it was not long before they both closed; the former is now a museum. South Crofty, the great survivor, remained the only tin mine at work but always with a bleak future. It closed on 6 March 1998, a tragic day in the long history of Cornish tin mining; the price of tin was around £3,300 per tonne.

CHAPTER THREE

CORNISH MINING LANDSCAPES

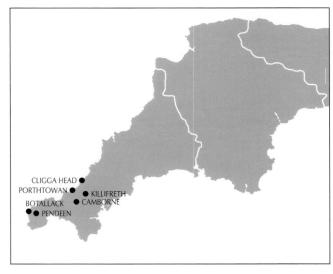

FOUR OF THE VIEWS selected here show abandoned mines with their empty engine houses, which are as synonymous with the Cornish landscape as fishing coves, sandy beaches, rugged headlands or granite moorlands. Of the hundreds of engine houses which once stood on the mines across Cornwall and Devon, a good many have survived in some form, varying from total preservation to a crumbled ruin. To this writer at least, they cannot be viewed in isolation and the derelict acres of waste dumps, turned-over ground and wall-ringed shafts are equally expressive of the great mining years.

The 'Cornish mining landscape', it would seem, is not complete without its roofless engine houses (although in decreasing numbers), which are a symbol of the county's unique industrial past. Some of the best of these distinctive ruins are found in dramatic situations, like the cliff tops where they are preserved at Botallack, Levant, Wheal Coates and Wheal Prosper, and are familiar from Cornish postcards, calendars or popular guidebooks. The two famous Crowns engine houses of the Botallack Mine, perched on a crag down near the ocean, must have been photographed hundreds of times and from many angles. Nevertheless, this book includes an example: it is not just a contemporary view, but also one which is firmly dated - to the minute too! Many other photographs can be compared to show changes at the site over the years. In fact, Jack Rhodes returned here for the Geological

Survey in August 1945, although he did not record the day and time (Photographs A8077-9).

One of the finest views of the Cornish mining scene of all time - indeed, one of the world's greatest mining landscapes - was that looking eastwards along the strike of the lodes from Dolcoath Mine across the Red River Valley to the Cook's Kitchen and Tincroft Mines and beyond. Burrow's famous photograph of 1893 was taken from the top of one of Dolcoath's stamping engine houses, a vantage point not used

Dolcoath Mine in 1893
J. C. Burrow's famous view of 'The Chief Mining District of Cornwall', looking east from Dolcoath Mine in 1893.
Cornish Studies Library

by Hall and MacAlister for the Geological Survey in 1904, and certainly unavailable in 1997. Burrow's view, being a little to the north, also shows on the left Dolcoath's old stamps engine and the new Californian stamps mill which was erected in 1892 with 40 heads, dressing equipment and electric lighting too. It is truly an incredible photograph, showing maybe 15 engine houses and 40 chimney stacks (see Burrow and Thomas, 1893). That there are so many is a small wonder when, for example, Carn Brea Mine alone is recorded to have had 18 steam engines in 1892. Several stacks served calciners, especially at Tincroft.

Changes have taken place in the intervening 11 years down to 1904, for we see a new steel headframe at Dolcoath's Eastern (Valley) Shaft and new rock breaking equipment, but only the south end of that mine's Californian stamps mill, with a change or two, is visible. The stamps battery and dressing floors at Cook's Kitchen Mine have been demolished, although the engine beam and its two flywheels can be seen outside the stamps engine house. Operations had declined following the mine's take-over by Tincroft in 1895. Carn Brea and Tincroft were amalgamated in the following year.

Almost a reverse of this view, looking west from below Carn Brea, was taken by Geoffrey Ordish 30 years later in June 1934. This immensely moving photograph of a devastated mining field complements the earlier ones, showing a forest of dark chimneys and engine houses beyond, all derelict or idle with the exception of a single smoking stack at South Crofty Mine (see Jenkin, 1965, 51, or Embrey and Symes, 1987, 42).

The same place today (1997) is almost unrecognisable, although the surviving engine houses (50-inch pumping and 30-inch winding) at Chapple's Shaft on Cook's Kitchen Mine are key markers. There are only four other good engine houses left in the area but, amazingly, three contain beam engines - two of which were erected since Burrow's time. Much of the scene has become an industrial estate or is waste ground. Only the more modern South Crofty Mine stands out to the north (left) but is just outside the photograph. The outline of Carn Brea behind is unchanged.

The following photographs show the landscape of the Cornish mining industry at the end of its last great days, with dereliction already creeping in. The views of 1945 depict empty engine houses in the sort of scenes which we know so well today.

Dolcoath Mine in1997
The same view in 1997, with engine houses of Cook's Kitchen Mine surviving.

The Camborne Mining District

'The Chief Mining District in Cornwall' is how Burrow termed his photograph of this same view 11 years earlier, and several changes are observable if the two photographs are compared. The strip of ground visible here, just over a mile long and half a mile wide (1.6 km by 0.8 km), includes the setts of Cook's Kitchen, Tincroft, Carn Brea and East Pool, mines which gave up over half a million tons of copper ore and over 130,000 tons of black tin during the century down to the time of the photograph. Dolcoath, which is mostly behind the camera, was the richest of them all, yielding a further 248,000 tons of copper ore and 77,300 tons of black tin. At least 30 chimneys and 13 engine houses are visible. The dominating granite hill of Carn Brea, with its castle and monument, is seen on the right. Weather conditions on the day were 'sunshine through clouds' and a quarter-second exposure was used. This photograph was published as the frontispiece of Dines, 1956, Plate I.

D. A. MacAlister and T C. Hall, 1.00 p.m. 25 September 1904 [A37] from SW 661405

Just as Burrow and Thomas did in their book in 1893, a sketch is given to explain the 1904 view.

DOLCOATH MINE
1. Tuckingmill or Red River Valley, with roof of old smithy
2. pools and ragging frames of dressing floors
3. end of Californian stamps building
4. power house for pumping water for dressing
5. Eastern (Valley) Shaft headframe, with crushing plant on left

COOK'S KITCHEN MINE
6. Count House (said to be the oldest mine office in Cornwall)
7. pumping and winding engine houses at Chapple's Shaft
8. stamps engine house with site of dressing floors in front

TINCROFT MINE
9. man-engine house
10. engine house for Harvey's 70-inch pumping engine of 1890. Part of Carn Brea Mine visible behind, to right
11. crusher-whim engine house
12. north section of mine, with shafts, engine houses and calciner stacks

EAST POOL MINE
13. East Pool Mine

SLOPES OF CARN BREA
14. Great Western Railway (formerly Hayle Railway and West Cornwall Railway), with iron bridge over cutting
15. North Crofty Branch, a short siding from the original Hayle Railway (in use 1837-1948)
16. Wesleyan Methodist Chapel at Tregajorran (demolished and replaced by two bungalows in 1996)
17. Carn Brea hill, with castle (left) and summit monument of 1836 to local mineral owner Francis Bassett of Tehidy

Crowns engine houses, Botallack Mine

The very famous view of two engine houses far down the cliffs near the Atlantic swell, although the tide is out in this picture. The reason for this precarious siting was that the Botallack copper and tin mine ran out under the sea at this point. The engine house on the left contained a 30-inch pumping engine of about 1835, while the other one contained a winding engine of 1862 for hauling from the inclined Boscawen Diagonal Shaft (hidden behind). Because of limited space, the stack for the former is inside the house and the latter is just up the cliff. Botallack had been closed for 11 years when this photograph was taken, having succumbed to an all-time low in the price of tin. Apart from a passing steamship out at sea, the view is largely unchanged today. Thankfully, the engine houses were consolidated and preserved by the Carn Brea Mining Society in 1985. The Crowns engine houses have been photographed on many dates, and Rhodes took similar views in 1945, but it is an indication of their importance that the BGS collection includes a much earlier photograph (A8080) of the mine at work, taken by Gibson & Sons of Penzance and not by Geological Survey staff (see Dines, 1956, Plates IIA & B).

Botallack was often visited by celebrities, such as Prince Albert Edward and Princess Alexandra whose descent of the inclined shaft on 24 July 1865 was captured by the photographer Robert Preston of Penzance (see Thomas, 1988, 112-116).

T. C. Hall, 10.30 a.m. 9 May 1906 [A 243] SW362336

Cligga Head

This is more than a dramatic scene of the north Cornish coast. Cligga Head lies between St Agnes and Perranporth, where a small exposure of granite in the headland (left) is surrounded by mineralised killas which has been worked extensively for tin, copper and wolfram. The cliffs are honeycombed with old mine workings. In the past, some miners earned a living extracting ores from winter cliff-falls on the shore below. This distant view looks north from above Hanover Cove, and shows signs of industry on the skyline. There is the ruined engine house of Good Fortune, but the other features belong to an explosives factory. The pair of tall chimneys were on the nitric acid factory section, and protective bunds can be seen to the left. After 1891, dynamite was manufactured by the British and Colonial Explosives Co. here on the clifftop, then supposedly remote from Perranporth down the hill. Nobel's Explosives took over in 1893 and continued to make explosives until 1905. After a revival for munitions work during the Great War, the whole factory closed soon afterwards (Earl, 1978, 251-63). Later, Cligga Mine was

worked for tin and wolfram out on the head in 1938-44, and a Second World War airfield was built on the flat cliff tops, mainly to the right. This and other views taken around the St Agnes area (see Chapter Eleven) are believed to be the earliest photograph in the British Geological Survey's 'A' Series.

J. B. Scrivenor, June 1903 [A84] SW 739537

The Porthtowan or Tywarnhayle Valley

The 'engine house in the Cornish landscape' is well seen in the Porthtowan valley. The view looks north west down the valley from above Wheal Bassett Farm, and shows the engine houses of Wheal Ellen (bottom, with castellated chimney stack) and United Hills or Tywarnhayle Mines up on the valleyside. The latter housed a 70-inch pumping engine at John's Shaft. The view is little changed today, although Wheal Ellen's engine house has lost its gable end (see Stanier, 1988, 5). To descend the lane into the valley towards the sea is a wonderful experience. This is copper-mining country and the valley retains all the atmosphere of mining dereliction and has not suffered the 'restoration' and developments experienced in the great Camborne-Redruth district, just to the south.

J. Rhodes, August 1945 [A8063] SW 703469

Pendeen water supply

While photographing Geevor Mine (Chapter Seven), Rhodes also captured something of the flavour of everyday life in and around the Pendeen tin mining district in the far west of Cornwall. There was still no mains water supply at this date, and here we see one local source - a spout emerging from an old adit of Boscaswell Downs Mine. Sam May has backed in his horse Polly to fill up his water cart before selling the water at a penny per bucket around the village. He had worked in Geevor Mine, as did his brother, but became a part-time farmer and water carrier. Boscaswell Terrace, along the main road through Higher Boscaswell, is in the background. The site of the water spout is still there beside the lane (now with a tarmacadam surface) from Pendeen to Calartha and Pendeen lighthouse. Rhodes recorded this view was to the north east. It is in fact to the south east.

J. Rhodes, August 1945 [A8039] SW 384347

Killifreth and the St Day Mining District

Although taken 53 years ago, this scene of empty engine houses marching across the Cornish mining landscape is still recognisable today. To the east of Redruth lies an extensive run of mining ground, and we are looking south from the Redruth-Chacewater road towards the Killifreth mine's notable engine house at Hawke's Shaft. Its distinctive tall and slender chimney stack is the result of heightening to improve the draught for the boilers of a large 85-inch pumping engine and a winder during a reopening of 1913. This tin mine worked until 1920, but the pumping engine remained in its house until scrapped during the war just a few years before this photograph. Also recently demolished was a winding engine house which would have been seen just left of the engine house (see Ordish, 1968, 14). Leftwards, the next two engine houses (pumping and winding) are on Unity Wood Mine, and beyond is a stack on Poldice Mine. On the extreme left is the clock tower of Consolidated Mines (1819-70), the site of the world's richest copper lode in its time. This view was published in Dines, 1956, Plate IXA.

J. Rhodes, August 1945 [A8120] SW 734442

CHAPTER FOUR
UNDERGROUND MINING SCENES

THE BGS PHOTOGRAPHS do not match the superb quality seen in the pioneering plates of J.C. Burrow, a professional photographer who persevered against immensely difficult conditions to produce some of the most dramatic underground mining scenes ever seen (Burrow and Thomas, 1893). Nor, in general, do the BGS plates have the interest of miners at work because they were mostly intended to show the nature of the geology and mineral lodes encountered underground; this they achieve well. However, some of those selected here do include miners as a focus of interest. Burrow described graphically the problems and practicalities of underground photography in the 1890s, in his book and a paper read to the Royal Geological Society of Cornwall (Burrow, 1894). A most useful summary of the subject as a whole has been given by Watton (1990).

Most of the underground scenes are in the important Cornish tin mines, and a wolfram mine, so the following outline is mainly concerned with them. The techniques of Cornish hard-rock mining have been described in greater detail, for example, by Earl (1994). The last two photographs, however, show slightly different methods for mining micaceous haematite and barytes in Devon.

The mineral lodes in the Cornish mining districts are often parallel, with a general east-north-east trend; so-called caunter lodes cut these at an angle, while crosscourses trend north-south. With a few exceptions, such as the Great Flat Lode to

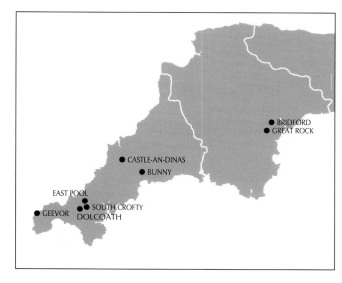

the south of Camborne, most lodes are steeply inclined. Their surface outcrop was recognisable to prospectors, but today they are marked by lines of derelict land and abandoned shafts. The same lode might pass through the 'setts' of several mines.

The principal method of working a mine was to sink a shaft, either following the lie of the lode or vertically to intercept it at depth. Levels were driven horizontally from the shaft to exploit the lode. The shallower parts of a mine were drained through an adit level which discharged the waste water through a portal sited down in a valley or at the foot of a sea cliff. Developments below adit level had to be drained constantly - in the period of this book, this was by plunger pumps worked by steam beam engines or electric pumps. Shafts sunk on a lode were seldom straight because of the vagaries of the lode, which gave added problems for pumping and haulage. Even vertical shafts may have changed direction once they reached the lode. Where necessary, shafts were lined with timberwork and divided into compartments, for pitwork (timber pump rod and cast-iron rising main), ladderway, capstanway and haulage or skipway. A deep shaft had pumps and balance bobs at intervals.

The depth of a mine and its levels was usually measured in fathoms (1 fathom = 6 feet or 1.83 metres), and this might be stated as either the depth 'below adit' or 'below grass'. Some of the deepest mines were around Camborne, with Dolcoath reaching 550 fathoms (1006 metres), Cook's Kitchen 430 fathoms (786 metres) and Carn Brea and Tincroft 390 fathoms (713 metres). South Crofty reached 470 fathoms (859 metres) deep.

Miners were either 'tributers', who engaged to take a share of the value of ore won from the lode, or 'tutworkers', who worked at a fixed price shaft sinking or level driving. They worked as a 'pare' or team in a section known as a 'pitch', and all underground work required the boring of shot holes for blasting. As can be seen in the earlier photographs this was still done by hand boring in some places, despite the mines having invested in compressed air rock drills, manufactured locally by Holman Bros. of Camborne, the Tuckingmill Foundry and others.

To win ore, levels were driven along the lode at intervals of 10-20 fathoms (18-36 metres). They were connected by short shafts ('winzes'), and the block of ore between was mined out in a 'stope'. Meanwhile, development levels were driven on ahead to explore and test the value of the lode. A cross-cut was a level driven through unproductive ground at right angles, either exploratory or to join up with another known lode. The width of stopes varied according to the lodes, which were narrow in the St Just and Pendeen area but spacious in Dolcoath or East Pool. They were worked downwards by 'underhand stoping' or upwards by 'overhand stoping'. In the latter, the blasted ore fell onto wooden platforms supported by timber 'stulls' and then into chutes ('mills') to load trams on the level below. Whichever way, the ore was trammed along a level to the shaft. From here, broken ore (and waste not backfilled in the stopes) was hoisted to the surface. Barrel-like iron kibbles were used in the earlier mines and small exploratory shafts of the twentieth century, but after

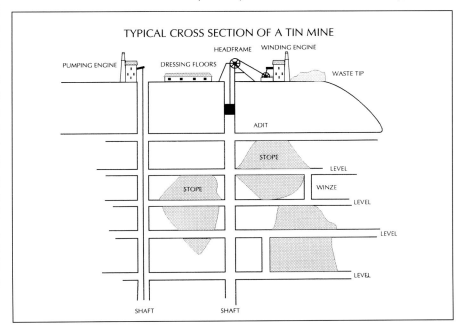

TYPICAL CROSS SECTION OF A TIN MINE

the 1850s larger wheeled skips holding up to 1½ tons were used. A 'lander' received these at the surface, knocking out a pin which opened a bottom door to release the ore. They were in turn replaced by self-dumping skips or cages carrying tram wagons. Wire ropes for haulage were the norm by the end of the nineteenth century. Winding at small and shallow shafts might be by waterpower or a horse whim. For the deeper mines, winding was by steam whims, worked first by rotative beam engines and later horizontal engines. There were electric winders in the twentieth century.

Access underground was traditionally by a ladderway, which was crippling for the men in the deepest mines. Much of this effort was relieved in the second half of the nineteenth century with the introduction of man-engines, whereby miners stepped on and off a rod rising and descending in the shaft. Some were still working in the early twentieth century (the breakage of the Levant man-engine in 1919, when 31 miners were killed, is well known), but they became obsolete with the adoption of haulage gigs (like skips) and cages - sometimes these could be exchanged for ore skips in the same shaft.

A Cornish miner's working clothes, seen in the earlier photographs, consisted of a thick flannel shirt, trousers and canvas coat, which would become stained red after a short time underground. A cotton cap on his head made a lining, when worn, for a helmet of felt impregnated and hardened with resin. The blackness underground was lit by a tallow candle stuck in a lump of special clay on the helmet. Spare candles were hung by their wicks from a coat button. In the working place underground, candles were also fixed to clay on a ledge, the end of a hammer handle or a ladder or other timberwork (this last was responsible for more than one serious fire!). Acetylene or carbide lamps were used as the twentieth century progressed, as seen in 1945 in Robinson's Shaft, South Crofty Mine. There followed improvements in safety helmets and the introduction of battery-powered electric headlamps.

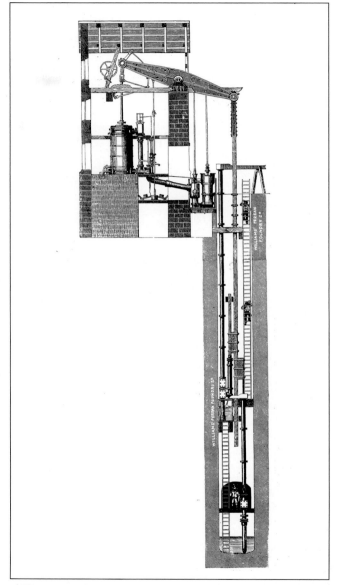

Williams Perran Foundry pumping engine and shaftwork
Courtesy Trevithick Society

25

Dolcoath Main Lode, 412 fathom level

No photographic collection of underground Cornish mining scenes would be complete without the inclusion of the famous Main Lode at Dolcoath Mine (SW 661403), which was the richest and most productive lode in the South West. It also extended eastwards into the Cook's Kitchen, Tincroft and Carn Brea Mines (see Chapter Three). Copper was mined from this lode down to about 200 fathoms (366 metres), below which there was rich tin. At depth, this great lode was found to vary in width between about 12 and 36 feet (3.6 -11 metres). The photograph was taken at the 412 fathom (754 metres) level, and shows an exposure at the hanging wall side of the Main Lode. The miner holds a candle in one hand, while a spare hangs from his jacket. Dolcoath suffered a severe fall of ground on this very level on 20 September 1893 when a supporting timber 'stull' was being strengthened where the lode was 30 feet (9 metres) wide. The massive timberwork was photographed by Burrow a short time before (see Burrow and Thomas, 1893, Plate 14). This photograph was published in Dewey (1935, Plate XA) and Dines (1956, Plate VIIIA).

D. A. MacAlister & T. C. Hall, 26 September 1904 [A60]

Working a stope at 200 fathoms in East Pool Mine

A posed photograph of a 'pare' of six miners in a stope at the 200 fathoms level, or 366 metres underground in East Pool Mine (Chapter Five). This is underhand stoping and it can be seen that the holes for blasting are is still being bored by hand at this date. One miner (almost concealed) holds the borer rod, giving it a half-turn between blows delivered by two sledgehammers. Note the spare rods behind the miners in the centre and extreme left; also the miners' helmets, the barrel, bottle and knapsack for 'croust'. Three men are holding candles (for the benefit of the photographer?) while another candle has been placed on the rock between the two working men.

D. A. MacAlister, 20 September 1904 [A61]

Bunny Mine

Bunny Mine (SX 00751) was a tin and wolfram mine in china clay country about 3 miles (5 kilometres) north of St Austell. It was active in the nineteenth century, first known as St Austell Hills in the 1830s, but was closed in 1874. This photograph was taken during a brief reopening in 1902-7, when 257 tons of black tin and 83 tons of wolfram were produced. The miner, or assistant accompanying the photographer, is standing at the top of a stope on No.1 lode, at the 58 fathom (106 metres) level and close to the bottom of the mine. Note his traditional miner's helmet and the candle lodged on a rock just above his head. The lode is above and to the left, while kaolinised granite can be seen on the right. No.1 was the main lode of ten and contained strings of quartz, cassiterite and wolfram. A96 is a companion photograph, taken in the central stope at the 50 fathom level (see Dines,1956, Plate XA).

D. A. MacAlister, November 1904 [A97]

The Coronation Lode, Geevor Mine

This view is at the east end of the 10th level on Coronation Lode and shows the main quartz leader (white) and other quartz-filled fissures with chlorite (dark) alongside and altered tin-bearing granite (above the hammer). Some drill holes for blasting can be seen at the end of the level on the left. The mineral lodes along the coastal mining district of St Just and Pendeen trend north-west and pass out under the sea. Geevor's lodes are narrow, from 12 to 18 inches (0.3 - 0.45 metres) so the miners had to blast additional rock on each side to enable them to work in the stopes. Other lodes worked at Geevor Mine (Chapter Seven) included the North and South Pig Lodes.

J. Rhodes, August 1945 [A8084]

27

In Robinson's Shaft at South Crofty Mine
An underground scene showing some action, instead of the finer points of the tin lode or other geological interest. Two miners are loading ore-laden tram tubs into a two-decker cage which has compartments of unequal size. An acetylene lamp is hanging from a hook in the centre, and the column of a cast-iron rising main is just visible in the pump and ladder way compartment on the left. The site is at a station in Robinson's Shaft at the 310 fathoms (567 metres) level. The headframe and engine house at the top of this shaft are seen at two dates, 1904 and 1945, in Chapter Five.
J. Rhodes, August 1945 [A8102]

28

Wolfram lode, Castle-an-Dinas Mine

Castle-an-Dinas was a twentieth-century mine with seven levels working along a north-south wolfram lode until 1957 (see Chapter Five). Here we see the lode at the 5th level, about 300 feet (91 metres) below and to the north of New or South Shaft. The lode is 3 feet (0.9 metres) wide and is seen in the roof of the level. Occasional black wolfram crystals occur here and there, and the sides of the level are of tourmalinised killas wall rock. Note the tub tram in the level. Other underground photographs, A8132-3 of the lode on the 5th level and A8137 on the 4th level, appear in Dines,1956, Plates XIB, XIIA and XIIB.

J. Rhodes, August 1945 [A8135]

Great Rock Micaceous Haematite Mine

This was a small mine, last worked until 1969, at an isolated location on the east side of Dartmoor (Chapter Twelve). It was worked from 17 adits and six shafts, exploiting 12 east-west lodes. This photograph is in Beadon Adit and shows the method of working known as 'hulking'. To prevent the soft and friable micaceous haematite in the narrow lode from being damaged by blasting, it is first extracted for about 6 feet (2 metres) in advance before the hard granite can be blasted to widen the stope to a working width (seen on the left). The operation is repeated as the heading progresses. The granite is highly chloritized at the lode walls. Published in Dines, 1956, Plate XIVB.

J. Rhodes, August 1945 [A8157]

On No.3 Vein, Bridford Barytes Mine

Bridford Mine (Chapter Twelve) was a near neighbour of Great Rock, but this time the ore is barytes and the lode is over 30 feet (9 metres) wide. The photograph is taken in a wide stope above the 380-foot (116 metres) level on No.3 Vein. The ore body is dipping to the right. It is one of five veins found here, trending approximately north north west. Note the two miners, a point of interest in an otherwise rather murky photograph. The mine was closed 13 years later. Another photograph (A8163) of the No.3 Vein at the same underground level, was published in Dines, 1956, Plate XVB.
J. Rhodes, August 1945 [A8165]

CHAPTER FIVE
SURFACE MINING SCENES

THERE IS A MARKED contrast between the sight of a 'knacked bal' with its forlorn, roofless engine houses and that of a living mine. On the latter, there was smoke, steam, noises of all kinds and at intervals the excitement of the accelerating motion of the sheave wheels atop the headframe, indicating the hauling of ores from the very depths of the mine. At shift changes, it was the miners being raised and lowered in the shaft. One might also see the slow but forceful rise and fall of the beam of a great pumping engine as it laboured away.

At the shaft of a late nineteenth or early twentieth-century Cornish mine, there was a large sturdy house containing the pumping engine. The engine house was built to last, with a thicker bob wall to carry the great weight of the beam, which is one reason for its survival, while the boiler house alongside was often demolished when the boilers were removed. Heavy timber pump rods descended the shaft from the outdoor end of the engine's cast-iron beam. Straddling the top of the shaft there were tall timber shears for lowering heavy pitwork (timbers, pumps, pump rods and pipes), worked by a capstan. This arrangement is well seen in the plates of Robinson's New Shaft in 1904 and the derelict East Pool & Agar in 1945.

The main headframe (originally timber) was also here. From the sheave wheels on top, the hauling ropes angled down towards a winding engine house set some distance back from the shaft. A large mine had engines at more than one

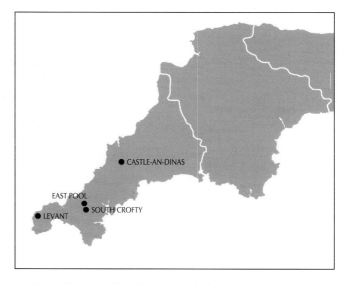

shaft, and the surface layout included a stamping engine, extensive dressing floors and perhaps even a calciner, flues and stack. Among all this there were leats and pools supplying water for the engines and floors, and tramways for taking ores from the shaft to the stamps or waste to the tips. There was also the account house (mine office) and even workers' cottages might survive among the mine buildings on the site. By the turn of the century, compressor houses were a new addition to the surface scene, as witnessed at Levant in 1906. The whole picture is illustrated in the famous panorama of the Camborne-Redruth district (see Chapter Three).

The surface of a working mine presents a generally untidy appearance with equipment of all types, size and condition lying around discarded or ready for use. For example at New Cook's Kitchen, Taylor's and Agar shafts, we see pipes, pump rods and even a small cement mixer.

The later photographs show how the surface of mines had changed by the mid-twentieth century. Although New Cook's Kitchen Shaft has a new steel headframe, old ways still hang on because the beam pumping engine alongside in its concrete house would still work for another five years. Taylor's Shaft is interesting for being an entirely twentieth-century project. Its timber headframe of the 1920s contrasts with the simpler gear and shears of earlier years seen at Robinson's Shaft and the derelict East Pool & Agar engine shaft. Again, the Castle-an-Dinas wolfram mine was a product of the twentieth century. The whole mine was just 25 years old when photographed in 1945.

Tincroft surface works

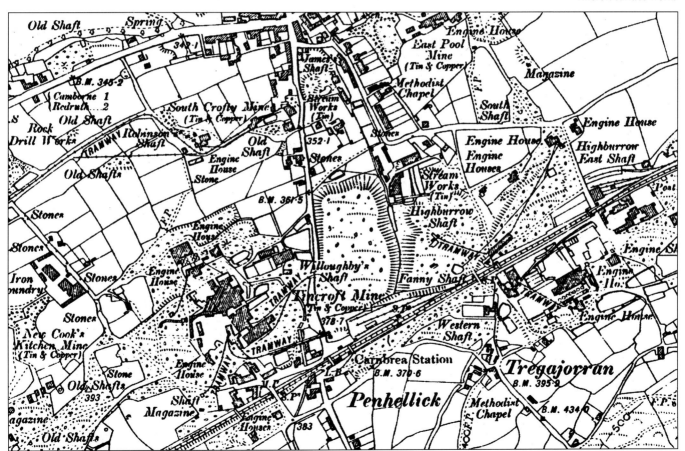

Levant Mine

Not the usual view of this well-known tin and copper mine, which was photographed from the inland side looking north east (see, for example, Trounson, 1981, plates 15-16). Instead, it looks up at the engine houses from a short way down the cliffs. It is also a photograph that can be dated very accurately. Note the headframe on Skip Shaft which served workings that extended out under the sea for over a mile. The small engine house contains an 1844 indoor winding beam engine, recently restored by Trevithick Society volunteers to work in steam. The chimneys of this and the pumping engine house behind are smoking away. The tall banded stack on the right was for the compressor house (just visible behind the account house), an ambitious structure built in 1901 for a Holmans four-cylinder cross-triple-expansion compressor to power drills and an underground winding engine. The ruins remain impressive today. The stamps engine house is in the centre and on the far left is the tall stack (just smoking) at the end of the arsenic flues. In 1906 Levant's 547 employees (359 underground) produced 457 tons of tin (worth £49,031), 2,140 tons copper ore (£8,819) and 234 tons of arsenic (£2,267). These figures demonstrate clearly the importance of tin against the low value of copper at that date, despite the much greater tonnage mined.

T. C. Hall, 3p.m. 9 May 1906 [A275] SW 368345

Miners at Palmer's Shaft, South Crofty Mine
This is a rare photograph in the BGS collection, showing a group of miners assembled outside the engine house at Palmer's Shaft. Note the helmets and candles carried by two miners in the front row. Sitting on a haulage gig or cage on the left are two men kitted out in clean working clothes - there is a strong suspicion that they may be Hall and MacAlister. On the extreme left of the shaft is the solid granite bob wall of the pumping engine house erected in the 1860s with a 60-inch engine. Behind is the gable wall of the winding engine house. Looking south east.
D. A. MacAlister & T. C. Hall, 1.30 p.m. 20 September 1904 [A38] SW 669413

Robinson's New Shaft, South Crofty Mine

A 3-second exposure gives superb clarity for this good side view showing the arrangement of pumping engine house, with raised beam, pump rod, capstan shears (for lowering pitwork) and temporary sinking headgear for a winding engine out of view to the left. The boiler house is on the far side of the engine house. The scene around the shaft was changed beyond recognition two years later when the old South Crofty Mine was reconstructed and new headgear was erected at Robinson's Shaft, with ore bins alongside. A sequence of photographs records this from start to finish (Trounson, 1980, plates 57-62). A photograph looking north from almost the same viewpoint as the BGS one was taken in the 1950s, when there was a steel headframe (Trounson, 1980, plate 67).

The 80-inch engine had been installed the year before this photograph, and was pumping from 2,021 feet (616 metres) when it was stopped on 1 May 1955 - the last Cornish beam engine to work on a Cornish mine. Electric pumps took over, but the fine engine is still preserved in its house. It was already old when brought here, having been built in 1854 by the Copperhouse Foundry at Hayle, worked for 20 years at Great Wheal Alfred, then Crenver and Wheal Abraham and finally Tregurtha Downs Mine near Goldsithney where it had acquired a new cylinder from Harveys of Hayle.

D. A. MacAlister & T. C. Hall, 5.00 p.m. 24 September 1904 [A39] SW 668413

New Cook's Kitchen Shaft, South Crofty Mine
The scene at South Crofty Mine some 40 years later, with just a wisp of smoke from the chimney stack. This engine house was erected in 1922 for a 90-inch pumping engine of 1873 and bought from the recently closed Grenville Mines. Although of traditional design, the engine house was of reinforced concrete for speedy construction because the mine was threatened with flooding after a fall had collapsed shafts in neighbouring East Pool the year before. This engine worked until 28 December 1950, when one side of the great cast-iron beam broke due to overloading. A large section narrowly missed falling down the shaft by wedging across the top. The rest of the engine was damaged and it was replaced by electric pumps stationed down the shaft.

The shaft has a steel headframe, as does Robinson's Shaft in the background. The winding house is on the extreme left. Self-dumping skips discharge into an ore bin, while waste rock is trammed onto a tip (left foreground). The headframe was replaced by a taller one and new powerful electric winder in 1970 to make Cook's Shaft the main hoisting shaft for South Crofty. In 1945, the shaft was 340 fathoms (622 metres) deep. By 1998 it was 420 fathoms (769 metres) with a decline at the bottom taking the mine down to 470 fathoms (859 metres). Published in Dines, 1956, Plate IVA.
J. Rhodes, August 1945 [A8101] SW 664409

Taylor's Shaft, East Pool Mine

A new shaft, named after East Pool Mine's manager Capt M. T. Taylor, was begun on a new site in January 1922, eight months after a serious collapse of ground had destroyed Engine Shaft to the south. The sequence of building was: first a temporary headgear (for shaft sinking), then the chimney, main headgear, boiler house, compressor house and finally the engine house (see Trounson, 1980, plates 110-114). The massive 90-inch pumping engine had been built by Harveys of Hayle in 1892 for Carn Brea Mine, from which it was acquired second-hand and installed in 1924. The beam weighs 52 tons and the whole engine is 125 tons. Although East Pool closed in 1945, the engine was kept going by South Crofty Mine until 1954, when electric pumps took over. At the time of the photograph, the shaft was 1,700 feet (518 metres) deep. The engine house is just visible behind the timber headframe. We also see the boiler house between the shaft and chimney stack which has the unusual white initials EPAL, for East Pool & Agar Ltd., and the trade name for the mine's arsenic. The gable end of the winder house is on the right. On the left is the old ore bin from which ore was taken by tramway to a mill in the Tolvaddon Valley. This was replaced in 1934 by an overhead ropeway. A length of timber pump rod lying on the ground (left) gives an impression of its size. Published in Dines, 1956, Plate VIA.

J. Rhodes, August 1945 [A8110] SW 674419

Taylor's Shaft, East Pool Mine in 1988

The site has since become an industrial heritage centre.

Michael Messenger

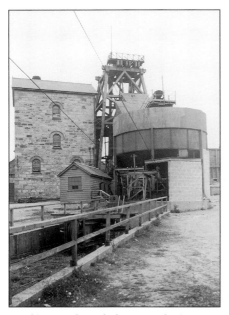

Ore bin at Taylor's Shaft, East Pool Mine

The circular ore bin with a conical base delivers ore raised from the shaft to tubs carried by the overhead ropeway to the dressing mill at Tolvaddon. In the foreground is part of the tension unit of the overhead ropeway. These were constructed in 1934 and worked for 11 years. Note the concrete block wall - a sign of the times and a contrast to the massive granite construction of the Taylor's engine house on the left. The mine closed at about the time of the photograph. The site, including the 90-inch pumping engine in its house, is now in the care of the National Trust and managed by the Trevithick Trust, with the former compressor house developed as a visitor centre for the discovery of Cornish mines, engines and industrial archaeology.

J. Rhodes, August 1945 [A8111] SW 674419

East Pool & Agar Mine

The end of a mine: the working headframe of Taylor's Shaft is in the background, but here the engine house and headgear at Engine Shaft are already derelict. The house contained the 90-inch Robartes' Engine bought from East Wheal Rose lead mine in 1886 along with five boilers. New pitwork and pumps were put in the shaft and the engine was named after Lord Robartes, the mineral owner in 1888. The beam broke within a year but was quickly replaced by Harveys of Hayle. The engine worked until 1922, stopped for two years and last worked in 1924-8. It remained idle and derelict until it was scrapped just three months after this photograph was taken. Note the banded brick chimney stack, deteriorating slate roof, the central clock and slit windows, a rare design but one still surviving in large engine houses at Tregurtha Downs and East Wheal Rose. The photograph shows the beam which has lost its pump rod (lying in the grass), the timber shears and the simple headframe worked from a winder out of sight. Left foreground, are the foundations of the rock breaker shed seen in another view taken 'probably in the second decade of this century' (Trounson,1981, plate 107). A fine photograph, undated, shows this house in relation to three others along Agar Road towards Pool (Trounson, 1968, 24-5). The site is now a supermarket and car park.

In 1945, three other large pumping engines were still working within a quarter-square mile area at East Pool and South Crofty. If they had survived just a little longer, perhaps all might have been preserved along with a fourth engine, the Holmans rotative winding engine of 1887 at Michell's Shaft.

J. Rhodes, August 1945 [A8109] SW 674416

North Shaft, Castle-an-Dinas Mine

This was a wolfram mine, worked for nearly a mile along a north-south lode beneath the hill of Castle-an-Dinas. It was not discovered until 1915 and a trial shaft was sunk on the north side of the hill in the following year. Full mining development began in 1918 by the South Crofty Co., when 46½ tons of wolfram were recovered. Between then and 1935, four adit levels were driven from the north side to exploit the lode and annual production increased to around 250 tons. The mine closed in 1957 after the price of wolfram fell heavily. This view shows North or Old Shaft, sunk in 1935 to serve the 3rd and 4th Levels, worked by a single-drum steam hoist. To the left of the timber headframe is the bin for ore raised from the shaft. In the foreground is the tension member at the end of an overhead ropeway delivering ore from South Shaft to the dressing mill (out of view to the left). Photograph A8140 shows the interior of the mill. The workshops are seen in the background to the right of the headframe. Looking north.

J. Rhodes, August 1945 [A8138] SW 947628

South Shaft, Castle-an-Dinas Mine

As the mine was deepened and extended southwards, New or South Shaft was sunk on the southern slope of the Castle-an-Dinas hill to 415 feet (126 metres) so that new development could take place down to a 7th level. A steam winding engine is behind the timber headframe, and a pump rod can be seen connecting the shaft with the pump house (containing an oil engine) on the right. The shaft contained the last Cornish pump to be installed anywhere in the world, made by Bartle & Sons at Tuckingmill. Waste rock raised in the shaft is trammed along a gantry to a dump on the left. Ore goes into the ore bin in the centre, and is fed into tubs on the overhead ropeway (worked by a steam engine) which passes through an iron age fort on the summit to the mill on the north side. Looking south, conical china clay tips around St Dennis are just visible on the skyline. Published in Dines, 1956, Plate XIA.

J. Rhodes, August 1945 [A8139] SW 945620

CHAPTER SIX
TIN ORE DRESSING

RICHER TIN ORES MIGHT contain 40 per cent black tin or more, but yields were normally much lower. When prices were high enough, as little as one per cent or 22 lb (9.96 kg) per ton became economical, but in all cases it is clear that large quantities of ore had to be mined and dressed. The object of ore dressing is to produce a final concentrate of black tin containing up to 60-70 per cent tin. The processes of gravity separation can be seen in these photographs of Dolcoath and South Crofty, with others at Geevor and Treveddoe in Chapters Seven and Eight.

Much has been written on the subject, from the eighteenth century when Borlase and Pryce described water-powered stamps and dressing and re-dressing in buddles and kieves, to the nineteenth century when modifications and advances were described by observers including Henwood, Henderson and Hunt. These have been summarised by Michell (1978), while dressing is also covered by Earl (1994). Eight of the ten 1904 photographs in this book accompanied MacAlister's notes on tin ore dressing in the Camborne area, published two years later (Hill and MacAlister, 1906, 262-274). He described dressing machinery currently in use and noted that there had been considerable improvements in the preparation of black tin for market in recent years. However, no two mines employed exactly the same process, although the principle was similar at the larger mines. Another discussion of tin

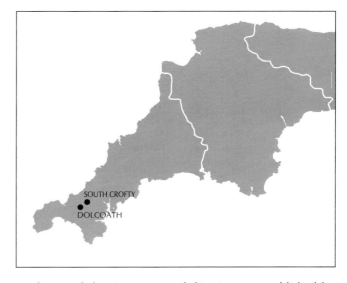

crushing and dressing at around this time was published by Fawns (1912, 199-227), who also used six of the BGS photographs (all uncredited) and an almost identical one of Dolcoath's Frue vanners credited to J. C. Burrow.

Once raised to surface, the ore was broken down with sledge hammers or mechanical stone breakers to remove as much waste rock as possible before being fed to the stamps for crushing. The old CORNISH STAMPS were a common sight in the tin mining districts where their deafening roar was heard

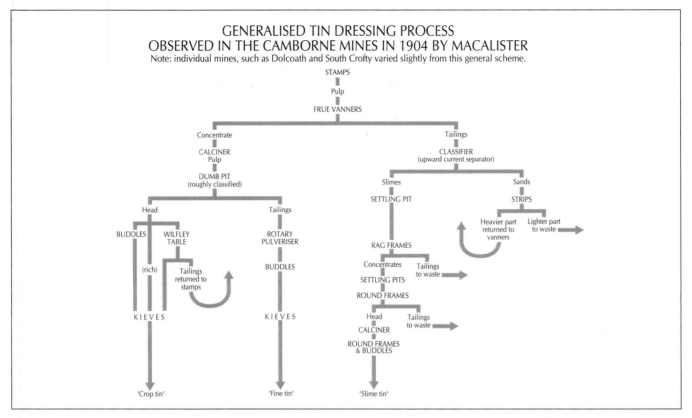

GENERALISED TIN DRESSING PROCESS
OBSERVED IN THE CAMBORNE MINES IN 1904 BY MACALISTER
Note: individual mines, such as Dolcoath and South Crofty varied slightly from this general scheme.

STAMPS
Pulp
FRUE VANNERS

Concentrate — Tailings

CALCINER
Pulp

CLASSIFIER
(upward current separator)

DUMB PIT
(roughly classified)

Slimes — Sands

SETTLING PIT — STRIPS

Head — Tailings

Heavier part returned to vanners — Lighter part to waste

BUDDLES — WILFLEY TABLE

ROTARY PULVERISER

RAG FRAMES

(rich) — Tailings returned to stamps

BUDDLES

Concentrates — Tailings to waste

SETTLING PITS

ROUND FRAMES

KIEVES — KIEVES

Head — Tailings to waste

CALCINER

ROUND FRAMES & BUDDLES

'Crop tin' — 'Fine tin' — 'Slime tin'

day and night. The early stamps were turned by waterwheels, and a succession of small stamping mills could be found along many valley streams. More powerful rotative steam engines were applied from the early nineteenth century. Cornish stamps had a frame holding sets of three or more vertical lifters of timber or iron, on the bottom of which was a heavy iron head. Projecting tappets on the lifters allowed a revolving barrel with cams to raise and release them in rapid succession, about 50 strokes per minute. The stampheads fell in an iron mortar box or coffer, into which ore was fed with water. The resulting fine crushed material or 'pulp' passed out through perforated plates of fine gauge.

Iron cam barrels could be bolted together to extend a stamps battery; in 1904, for example, we see up to 84 stamps worked by one engine at Wheal Grenville (Chapter One). In 1870, two engines at Dolcoath worked batteries of 120 and 60 stamps each, and a further 20 were worked by waterwheel in winter. Many smaller mines and streamworks continued to use water stamps well into the twentieth century if the water was available, such as at Treveddoe (Chapter Eight). Each Cornish head weighed around 700 lb (317 kg) and could process about 17 cwt (863 kg) per day.

Two improved types of stamps were in operation by 1904. CALIFORNIAN STAMPS were heavier, faster and could stamp

41

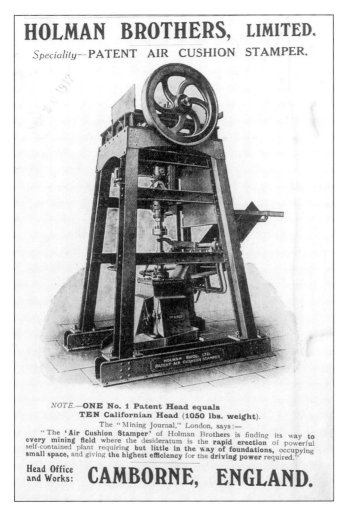

Patent PNEUMATIC STAMPS, by which compressed air drove the stamp heads down instead of just letting them drop, were built after 1871 by Harveys of Hayle and Holmans of Camborne. One head was said to be the equivalent of ten Californian heads and they could deal with even greater quantities of ore just at a time when the mines needed to increase efficiency to stay alive. They were used at Dolcoath.

However, investment was lacking at many mines and so Cornish stamps with their low maintenance and repair costs were still working in the 1904 photographs, 'an exceedingly interesting survival of the early days of crushing by machinery' (Fawns, 1912, 199). Rotating ball mills or tube mills containing scrap iron were tried for crushing or treating coarser sand, but they were often discarded in favour of stamps batteries.

The pulp was concentrated after leaving the stamps. It may have been first settled in long pits or it was sent direct to round buddles. These are seen at Wheal Grenville (Chapter One), but they had been dispensed with at Dolcoath and South Crofty, which had large sets of Frue vanners. FRUE VANNERS were invented in the United States in 1874 and became widespread in Cornwall by the turn of the century. They could treat some

up to three times more ore, while their self-rotating heads allowed for even wear. Capacity was increased by 29 per cent at Dolcoath in 1892, when 40 were installed. Each head of 800 lb (362 kg) had a 9-inch (23 cm) drop, delivered 80 blows a minute and could handle 1½ to 3 tons of hard ore a day. Each mortar box had five stamps and each set of ten was driven by separate belting, taking power from an engine.

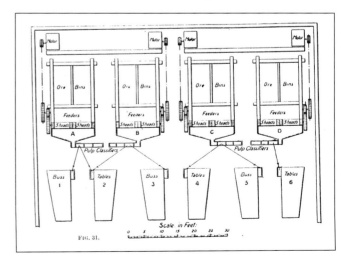

Fig. 31.

pulp which was less suitable for buddles. The WILFLEY TABLE was a type of shaking table which produced a variety of grades in the discharge. These popular tables replaced buddles on many mines. Four Frue vanners or four Wilfley tables could concentrate the pulp from ten stamps and each could treat 5-10 tons per day. Other types of shaking tables included Buss tables; these and Frue vanners served the new Californian stamps at South Crofty.

ROUND BUDDLES were a simple and effective means of concentrating the pulp. The most common were Convex buddles, which appeared after about 1848. They were circular, cement-lined pits up to 22 feet (6.7 metres) in diameter and 1½ feet (0.46 metre) deep. Buddles could treat up to 2 tons per hour each, but they were labour-intensive and had to be stopped while they were dug out. Buddles with a larger diameter treated poorer slimes. Concave buddles further concentrated the head from the convex buddles.

Very fine slimes were concentrated on slowly revolving ROUND FRAMES which were introduced in 1870 and remained important for much of the first half of the twentieth century. An improvement seen at Dolcoath was the ACME TABLE, an automatic revolving slimes table with two decks, concave and convex. RAGGING or RAG FRAMES were used for treating the finest slimes. Long lines of these were part of large dressing floors like Dolcoath, but were also common along with round frames at the tin salvage works downstream from the mines (Chapter Eleven).

CLASSIFIERS were used to sort material at different stages before it passed on for further dressing. Perhaps the simplest form was the DUMB PIT, illustrated on page 47. The CORNISH CLASSIFIER or UPWARD CURRENT SEPARATOR was more effective. It was a downward pointing conical box, inside which an upward jet of water carried the lighter material away while the heavier particles settled to an exit at the bottom. The size collected could be altered by regulating the amount of feed and speed of the jet (see Treveddoe,

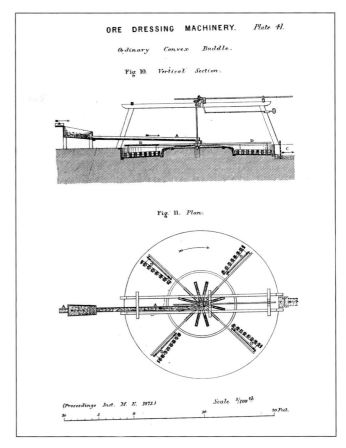

ORE DRESSING MACHINERY. *Plate 41.*

Ordinary Convex Buddle.

Fig 10. *Vertical Section.*

Fig. 11. *Plan.*

(Proceedings Inst. M. E. 1873.) *Scale* 1/100th

Chapter Eight). More sophisticated classifiers were the STOKES HYDROSIZER which is seen in 1945 at Geevor (Chapter Seven) and Hemerdon (Chapter Nine).

KIEVES were large tubs in which the tin ore was given a final enrichment by 'tossing' and 'packing'.

CALCINERS were erected on many mines, to burn off impurities such as sulphides at some stage in the dressing process. The Brunton's calciner was important for arsenopyrite. The concentrate, known as 'whits', was dropped onto the centre of a revolving firebrick hearth. While it was roasting, 'rabble arms' moved the material to the outside from which it fell and was collected. There was a long flue to a chamber (labyrinth or 'lambreth') where the arsenious oxide condensed and crystallised as a 'soot', to be dug out by hand. Arsenic became a valued product around the turn of the century. A fine example of a calciner still survives in 1998 in the Portreath valley (Chapter Eleven).

WOLFRAM SEPARATION from the cassiterite was necessary at the mines where it occurred, at first as an impurity and later as a valued tungsten mineral for hardening steels.

Having a similar specific gravity to the tin, this was not easy in the buddling processes. The Wetherell electro-magnetic separator was found to work effectively at East Pool and South Crofty Mines and could treat about 10 tons of concentrates a day. After the ore with tin and wolfram had been calcined it travelled on a belt under four electro-magnets. The first two picked out the iron and iron oxides, while the next two, being stronger, picked up the wolfram.

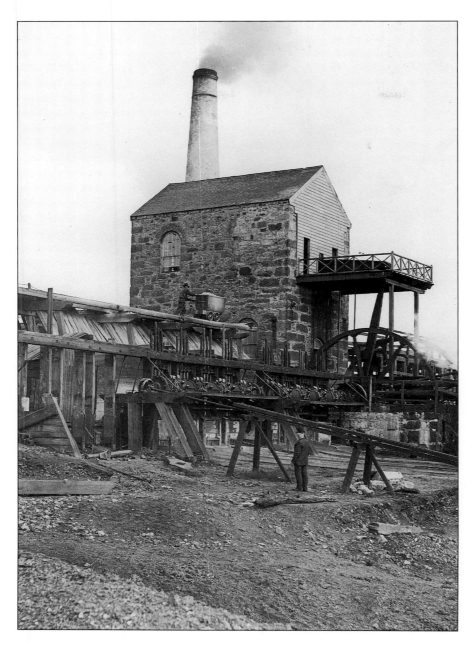

Cornish stamps at South Crofty Mine
South Crofty had 60 heads of Cornish stamps, worked by a 40-inch engine, which was 32 years old at the time of this photograph. Note the smoking chimney stack, the beam, sweep rod, two flywheels and stamps batteries on both sides; on this side there are eight sets of four stamps each, with space to extend to the left (there was a planned capacity of 100 stamps here). Above, a worker is about to tip ore from a tram tub into the feed bins. Three years later, the stamps were replaced by 40 Californian stamps erected on the far side and the engine house was demolished. See also the stamps and round buddles at Wheal Grenville (Chapter One). First published in Hill and MacAlister, 1906, Plate XIII. Looking south east.
D. A. MacAlister and T. C. Hall, 4 p.m. 24 September 1904 [A43] SW 663410

Californian stamps at South Crofty Mine

Forty-one years later. A view showing the cam-shaft gallery of the Californian stamp battery in the mill at South Crofty Mine. These replaced the Cornish stamps seen in the previous plate, and were powered by electricity from a local supply - this was deemed to be a more flexible source of power and worth the investment. Note the massive timber frames and the nature of the cams and rotating lifters in double sets of five. The workings of the first 40 head of Californian stamps and new concentrating tables erected at the same time were described by Fawns (1912, 206-8).

J. Rhodes, August 1945 [A8107] SW 663410

Frue vanner house at Dolcoath Mine

An impressive view of 24 Frue vanners, representing the 27 which were introduced here at Dolcoath in 1898. Frue vanners had a continuous belt of rubber which moved slowly against the flow of the pulp being fed on; they were also given a shake. Although they could treat a feed with a wide range of particle sizes without initial classification, one disadvantage was that they produced a concentrate and tail, but no middlings. This photograph required a two-minute exposure. First published in Hill and MacAlister, 1906, Plate XIV.

D. A. MacAlister and T. C. Hall, 12.30 p.m. 29 September 1904 [A46] approx SW 662406

Frue vanner at South Crofty Mine

This is a good detailed photograph in the dressing mill at South Crofty, showing the working of a Frue vanner with the feed for the pulp and distributors for fresh water flow, and the pale bands of tin concentrate coming off the top end of the belt. The vanner can be adjusted for inclination and speed. Note also the two workers and the scoop on the floor, a handy tool used in and around all dressing mills. Looking north west, a 30-second exposure was used. Photograph A45, taken 15 minutes later, shows an end view of the row of Frue vanners. *D. A. MacAlister and T. C. Hall, 4.15 p.m. 24 September 1904 [A44] approx SW 663410*

Dumb Pit at South Crofty Mine

The dumb pit was a form of classifier. This photograph shows it to be a small convex buddle with no moving parts. Pulp is fed in by a wooden trough or launder to the centre and the largest (heaviest) particles are deposited first, becoming smaller towards the outside. The time-exposure gives a good impression of the pulp spreading in the pit. When full, the dumb pit will be dug out carefully so that each size can be further buddled. Note the Cornish shovel behind. First published in Hill and MacAlister, 1906, Plate XIX. *D. A. MacAlister and T. C. Hall, 3.45 p.m. 24 September 1904 [A48] approx SW 663410*

Wilfley table at Dolcoath Mine

Installed at Dolcoath in 1896, the Wilfley table is a rectangular table slightly inclined towards the discharge side, sometimes covered with linoleum with small wood 'riffles', and shaken along its length. The pulp is fed on at the far corner (near the figure) and flows in a thin sheet of water diagonally across the table and separates into concentrates, middlings and tailings which are caught in separate launders as they come off to be collected in three tubs (foreground). The table worked best if the material was classified first to obtain grains of uniform size. Note the belt drive for the oscillating motion. One-minute exposure. Looking south west. First published in Hill and MacAlister, 1906, Plate XV.

D. A. MacAlister and T. C. Hall, 2.45 p.m. 24 September 1904 [A47] approx SW 662406

James table at South Crofty Mine

This is a later photograph of another form of table, which was shaken diagonally in the direction of the riffles. The head of tin concentrate is seen as a narrow light band crossing the table diagonally towards the camera and passing over the end of the table just to the right of the near corner. The darker band on the left of this is the middling product consisting of cassiterite particles adhering to quartz and heavy minerals such as iron oxides, tourmaline, etc. Lighter waste minerals, including quartz, appear as a pale area on the far left of the table where they have been carried over the riffles and will pass to tailings. Note also the inclination of the James table and the water feed at the top.

J. Rhodes, August 1945 [A8108] approx SW 663410

Convex buddles at Dolcoath Mine

Two convex buddles, looking south east. A hand-filled hopper on the left feeds pulp over a cone in the centre, and three rotating arms with adjustable brushes help distribute the material as it is washed across the gently sloping floor of the buddle. A fourth, smaller brush works the slope of the cone. The lighter fines are washed out towards the buddle's perimeter, while the heavier tin is concentrated near the centre. Having been nearly filled, the buddle behind has had its rotating arms removed so it can be dug out carefully in 'rings' according to the value of the concentrate (see Treveddoe, Chapter Eight). The richest concentrates might be re-buddled if necessary. 30-second exposure. First published in Hill and MacAlister, 1906, Plate XVII.

D. A. MacAlister and T. C. Hall, 3 p.m. 24 September 1904 [A49] approx SW 662406

Concave buddle at South Crofty Mine

A good view of a concave buddle at work. The pulp is fed from the right into the centre, and then at least five rotating arms deliver it to the outside of the buddle. Brushes are hanging from only two of the arms. Note the gearing and spindle drive from above. Behind, can be seen a convex buddle and large round frame (right). Looking south east, with a 30-second exposure. First published in Hill and MacAlister, 1906, Plate XVIII.

D. A. MacAlister and T. C. Hall, 4 p.m. 24 September 1904 [A50] approx SW 663410

Acme table at Dolcoath Mine

The Acme Combined Concentrating Table was a double-deck revolving slimes table, concave on the upper deck and convex on the lower, thus treating the pulp twice and automatically too. Further advantages claimed were that the frame required little attention once adjusted, there were no middlings and it required only half a horsepower to drive it. Looking south. One-minute exposure. First published in Hill and MacAlister, 1906, Plate XVI.

D. A. MacAlister and T. C. Hall, 4 p.m. 24 September 1904 [A52] approx SW 662406

Kieves at Dolcoath Mine

In a final stage of enrichment, the highly concentrated ore was stirred or 'tossed' with water in these large tubs or kieves. This was done manually or by paddle gear. After being allowed to settle, the tub was 'packed' or struck on the side by a hammer, bar or, as seen here, automatic knockers worked from above. The lighter material was then skimmed from the top and the rich concentrate underneath was dug out ready for sale to the smelters. A 30-second exposure, looking south west. First published in Hill and MacAlister, 1906, Plate XX.
D. A. MacAlister and T. C. Hall, 2.55 p.m. 24 September 1904 [A51] approx SW 662406

51

Ragging frames at Dolcoath Mine

An interesting outdoor view of part of Dolcoath's dressing floors in the Red River or Tuckingmill valley, showing settling pits and ragging frames (foreground), an enclosed waterwheel, disused convex buddles (left of the wheel) and a variety of raised launders. The stamps engine house is seen in Burrow's famous photograph and is the lower one in Gibson's photograph which looks south west across the valley floor up to the centre of Dolcoath Mine on the high ground above (see Jenkin, 1948, 192). Such a scene is more typical of the many tin salvage works all the way down the Red River (see Chapter Eleven). Looking north west. *D. A. MacAlister and T. C. Hall, 1 p.m. 17 September 1904 [A53] SW 662406*

CHAPTER SEVEN
GEEVOR MINE

THE GEEVOR TIN MINE overlooks the Atlantic from a narrow coastal shelf at Pendeen in the far west of Cornwall. It was the last working mine in the once very active St Just tin and copper mining district, where the abandoned levels of nearby Botallack and Levant mines extend for over a mile under the sea. There has been mining here since at least the sixteenth century, and there is some archaeological evidence to suggest even earlier activity. Workings were developed for tin during the nineteenth century, first as East Levant Mine until 1840, and then as North Levant in 1851-91. When the latter closed, the manager, Capt James Bennetts, took up part of the sett under the name of Wheal Geevor and worked the shallower parts in a small way. Within a few years, North Levant (Wheal Geevor) was exploring and stoping down to adit level and re-working the old waste tips for their mineral content. Success of this venture saw investment in 1904 by West Australian Gold Fields Co. Ltd. and the formation of North Levant and Geevor Ltd., directed by Oliver Wethered.

The true modern mine dates from 1911, when Geevor Tin Mines Ltd. was formed, to exploit a sett of 208 acres (84 ha) along the North and South Pig Lodes for about 1½ miles (2.4 km). Modern dressing plant was installed, shafts refurbished and exploration begun. Wheal Carne Shaft and Wethered Shaft were both around 600 feet (183 metres) deep. The latter was a three-compartment shaft, with an electric winding

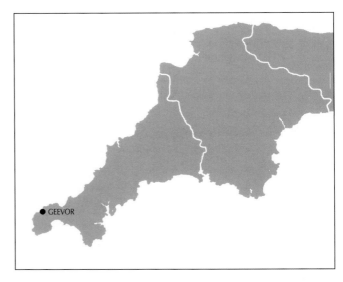

GEEVOR

engine which could hoist up to 160 tons of ore a day in self-dumping skips. About 60 per cent of Geevor's output was raised from Wethered Shaft. The ore was first carried by tramway to the mill lower down the slope, but after 1919 it was carried on a new 1,800-foot (550 metres) long overhead ropeway which could handle 200 tons per eight-hour shift. Upon arrival at the mill, the ore passed through Holman patent air cushion stamps before treatment. Victory Shaft, just above the mill, was begun in 1919 and sunk initially to 500 feet (152 metres), its name appropriately celebrating the conclusion of the Great War.

The risks of mining in a world of fluctuating metal prices were felt in 1921 and 1931, when low tin prices forced brief closures, but prudent development enabled Geevor to survive where other Cornish mines failed. There were even developments in the late 1930s, both underground and at surface where the pneumatic stamps were replaced by more modern jaw-crushers and a Symons cone. Geevor worked on through the Second World War, despite a constant shortage of skilled miners. In 1943, the total labour force above and below ground was about 450 men and 12 women. Output during the war declined. For example, in the year to the end of March 1939, some 266,450 tons of ore were milled to produce 1,033 tons of black tin (65 per cent tin), but by 1944 this had fallen to 65,181 tons milled and 681 tons of black tin. However, the mine came out of the war in relatively good shape despite shortages of labour and equipment. The following photographs show the state of Geevor right at the end of the war, at an important milestone in its life. They are mostly indoor views of the dressing plant, and make an interesting comparison with Dolcoath and South Crofty in 1904 (Chapter Six). The tables are modifications but the main difference is that crushing is now done in a ball mill. Output in 1945 was down again, to 577 tons of black tin. By good fortune, the workings of the mine at about this time, in March 1944, were described (Sevier, 1945). Reference to Seviers' flow diagrams will show how nothing is simple in a tin dressing mill, with tailings and middlings being returned to go round the circuit several times to enrich the final concentrate.

Geevor Mine's subsequent career is not without interest. In the following decade, the aerial ropeway was scrapped when Victory Shaft became the main hoisting shaft. In 1954, a new winder was installed and the original timber headframe was replaced by the taller steel one which survives today; the shaft continued down to 1,577 feet (481 metres), or below the 15 Level. Improved rock drills and mechanisation underground kept the mine in profit. In the 1960s, encouraged by rising tin prices, exploration took place to locate and develop new ore reserves, which included draining the old Levant Mine (which had closed in 1930) after first plugging a hole in the seabed with great difficulty. A new sub-incline shaft from 15 Level in Victory Shaft was sunk to 19 Level in 1975-77, and was extended even deeper and over a mile out under the sea. Levant's Skip Shaft on the cliff edge was used at this time (see Chapter Five), and there were developments in other shafts in the area.

The collapse of world tin prices in 1985 was disastrous for Geevor, which failed to obtain government help. The mine closed in April 1986, and nearly 300 miners lost their jobs, causing great hardship in the district. There was a brief reprieve in 1988 when Geevor was brought back into production in the hope of a recovery in tin prices. Work soon stopped again and after being kept on a care and maintenance basis, the pumps were finally stopped and the mine closed in 1990.

This was not quite the end of the mine. The site was purchased by Cornwall County Council and the area around the Victory Shaft and mill has been developed as a museum of, mainly, twentieth-century tin mining. Geevor Tin Mine is now under the management of the Trevithick Trust.

Geevor Mine from Carn Eane

A rather distant view, looking north west along the strike of the lodes from the collapsed collar of Carne Shaft (foreground). Wethered Shaft (left) and Victory Shaft can be seen, with the pylons of the overhead ropeway between. The tall chimney stacks in the distance belong to Levant Mine. The sea beyond is lost in the haze. Note also the winder house at Wethered Shaft, the scattered miners' cottages and small stone-walled fields which are typical of this part of west Cornwall. Published in Dines, 1956, Plate IIIA.

J. Rhodes, August 1945 [A8083]   from SW 382340

Timber headframe at Wethered Shaft

A fine picture of the timber headframe erected in 1911 over Wethered Shaft. Ore is hoisted by self-dumping skips and after the oversized pieces have passed through a rock breaker behind the headframe, it is stored in bins before being taken by overhead ropeway (not visible) to the mill near Victory Shaft. Wethered Shaft is about 600 feet (183 metres) deep and the headframe and timber-clad winder house still stand near the entrance to the mine from the main road between Trewellard and Pendeen.

J. Rhodes, August 1945 [A8089] SW 378341

Victory Shaft

Victory Shaft was commenced in 1919 and it was served with this timber headframe. The shaft was 1,446 feet (441 metres) deep in 1945, but was sunk deeper a few years later. Ore was originally raised in cages but self-dumping skips had been installed recently, discharging to an ore bin behind the headgear. For hoisting men, the skips were replaced by cages. Note also a timber pylon and the terminus of the overhead ropeway from Wethered Shaft, with the roof of the mill beyond. The ropeway ceased operation at about this time. Sited at the heart of the mine and close to the mill, Victory Shaft became increasingly important and the present tall steel headframe was erected here in 1954, when a new powerful electric winder replaced the old horizontal steam winding engine. Looking north.

J. Rhodes, August 1945 [A8090] SW 375345

Primary stage in the Geevor tin mill

Once raised from the mine, the ore goes through many stages before a final tin concentrate is achieved. It is first crushed, washed and screened, passed through a Symons cone-crusher and more screens before being deposited in a storage bin (photograph A8091). Here begins the primary concentration section of the mill. The ore is fed by an endless drag-chain belt (top left) to inclined vibrating Hummer screens (left) under water jets. Large material, over 24-mesh sieve size, passing over the screens enters the 7 x 3 foot (2.1 x 0.9 metres) Hardinge ball mill, the discharge from which passes back to the screens; all undersize from the screens is carried on to the concentrating plant. Despite the attentions of scrap-men after Geevor closed, this ball mill still survives.

J. Rhodes, August 1945 [A8092] SW 375346

Stokes hydrosizer

A rather difficult view in the mill, looking up at a Stokes hydrosizer. Pulp from the ball mill and screens passes to a rake classifier, the fine material from which goes to 15 vanners and the coarse material to this 10-spigot Stokes hydrosizer (the spigots are sized outlets). Its fine 2-spigot products pass to the vanners and the remaining 8-spigot products to James tables (see an example at South Crofty, Chapter Six).

J. Rhodes, August 1945 [A8093] SW 375346

Holman-Michell table

The heads from the James tables are treated on the Holman-Michell table for the removal of sulphides. This seems to have been an experiment installed since Sevier's description of the mine in 1944. It was a modification of the gravity table, devised by Frank Brice Michell of the Camborne School of Mines, and was a partly successful attempt to use flotation for the removal of sulphides. Note the air pipes across the table. It was claimed that sulphides could be removed at a coarser stage in tin dressing than by ordinary flotation, whilst tin losses were lower.

J. Rhodes, August 1945 [A8094] SW 375346

Slimes plant

Four concrete round frames (behind) are seen feeding two ordinary revolving round frames (middle distance), which in turn feed two vanners. The camera has focused on the end of one Frue vanner on the right; the light streaks on the belt are slime grade tin concentrate. The concrete round frames still survive in the mill.

J. Rhodes, August 1945 [A8095] SW 375346

Kieves on the final tin dressing floor

Concentrates from all sources are passed to flotation cells for the removal of sulphides and then to the tin dressing floor shown here, where they receive final treatment in convex buddles (centre) and kieve tubs (foreground and background). The material is stirred (tossed) in the kieves, the sides of which are beaten (packed) with mechanically operated mallets to cause the tin to settle to the bottom. The water is drawn off the top, impurites scraped off and the richest concentrate dug out from beneath. It is worth comparing the mallets with the knockers on the Dolcoath kieves in 1904 (Chapter Six).

J. Rhodes, August 1945 [A8096] SW 375346

The finished product: tin concentrates

Black tin concentrates (up to 70 per cent metal) are taken to this store room in wooden barrows. Here they are weighed and deposited on a floor of well laid smooth planks. Note the heater to keep the room dry, the clean swept floor, board for containing the concentrate, the wooden carriers, weighing scales and large stock of bags through the door behind. The heap of concentrates in the corner weighs about 7 tons and was said to be worth about £1,500 in 1945. Such an apparently insignificant pile of dirt would have been worth nearer £45,000 during the boom of the mid-1980s.

J. Rhodes, August 1945 [A8097] SW 375346

Trewellard Bottoms, below Geevor Mine

The waste discharged from most Cornish mines was treated again downstream in tin salvage works to reclaim the last possible amounts of tin (Chapter Eleven). Here at Geevor, the sheds of the streamers' works are seen in this view looking south east up the short valley to the mine. Victory Shaft and the dressing mill are prominent top left. Just above the streamworks is a small headframe at Thorn's Shaft. The sea cliffs are immediately behind the camera.

J. Rhodes, August 1945 [A8098] SW 373349

CHAPTER EIGHT
SMALL MINES AND TRIALS

MINERAL PROSPECTING HAS BEEN a feature of regions such as the South West throughout the centuries, always in the hope of winning new riches. As a result, alongside the big names in the roll-call of mines, there can be found hundreds of small undertakings and trials, some successful and others which came to little or nothing. These are the small mines which kept the tradition of mining going on quietly while the fortunes of their larger and better-known neighbours rose and fell. All the photographs here were taken in 1945.

Some lodes were not extensive enough to justify large investment but were quite adequate for a partnership of working miners to eke out a living. Many such ventures were run on a shoe-string, often with second-hand or even home-made equipment. Without the higher operating costs of large and expensive plant, these small mine workings were able to ride periods of low prices and seem to have worked on regardless. Shaft winding might be by horse whim, but wherever it was available, water was the cheapest source of power for pumping, stamping and working the dressing floors. The best example seen here is Treveddoe, which drew water via a leat from the Warleggan River in a deep valley on the southern edge of Bodmin Moor. Treveddoe was of one of several workings in that area dating from the inter-war years; although there were shafts and levels here, it was originally an opencast, similar to Mulberry and Wheal Prosper (Chapter

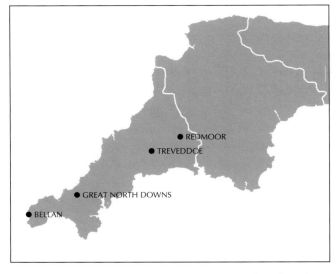

Nine). The BGS collection has some good plates showing the small self-contained tin dressing mill at Treveddoe.

In contrast, the working of the Bellan Mine in the far west was directly the result of wartime demands and it closed afterwards. Higher prices and the requirements of war encouraged mining operations and trials in many parts of the peninsula, although lack of money kept their scale to the minimum. These trials were either on new sites, or they involved the refurbishment and exploration of long-closed mines in a small and speculative way. The Ministry of Supply Non-Ferrous Development took an interest and the Cornish Tin Mining Advisory Committee was involved in prospecting trials in 1942-44, but very little in the way of minerals was produced. North Downs, 2 miles (3.2 km) north east of Redruth, was 'exceedingly promising' for wolfram (Trounson, 1989, 27). The area had contained some of Cornwall's main copper mines in the first half of the eighteenth century, but nothing came of trials to find tin or wolfram beneath the shallow workings. Another search for wolfram at Redmoor Mine near Callington was hardly any better. However, Redmoor was unusual in that altered killas slate was mined with a view to using it as a substitute for talc; in 1944-45 around 2,000 tons of powdered slate were used with bitumen

for the construction of advanced air strips (Polkinghorne, 1945, 269-270). The activities seen in the following photographs are a marked contrast to those at a larger mine such as Geevor (Chapter Seven).

Great North Downs Wolfram Trial

The presence of quartz-wolfram ore in dumps and field walls on part of the old Great North Downs Mine near Scorrier, led to investigations being made in 1938 and again during the Second World War. Paull's Shaft was opened in 1942 with this small headgear and some underground work was done at a depth of 120 feet (36 metres). Note the small corrugated iron winding shed and the kibble (bucket) drawn up just above the shaft. The shaft is on a vertical copper lode. At the same time, Footway Shaft of Wheal Rose was also opened. Both trials discovered some wolfram but there was no production. Looking north east. Published as the 'Scorrier Wolfram Prospect' in Dines, 1956, Plate VIIIB. *J. Rhodes, August 1945 [A8118]   approx SW 718444*

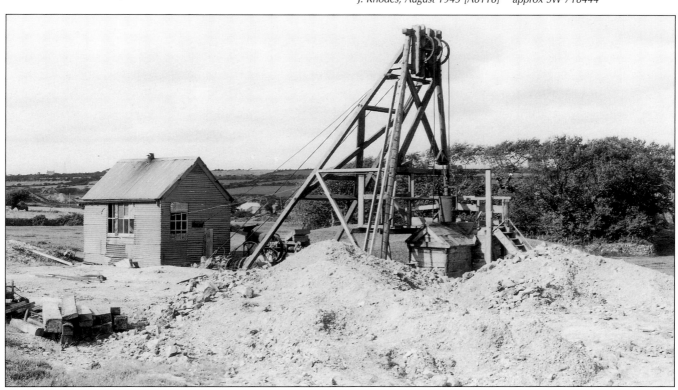

Redmoor Mine

Redmoor Mine, just south west of Kelly Bray near Callington, produced a variety of ores from the 1860s, including tin, copper, lead, silver, arsenic and wolfram. Never wholly successful, it was worked for tin and arsenic in 1888-92 as part of Callington United Mines which included neighbouring Holmbush and Kelly Bray Mines. Subsequent activity was mainly exploratory: just prior to the Great War, in about 1935 and under the supervision of the Ministry of Supply Non-Ferrous Development in 1941-45. The buildings in this view belong to the mill of this last working. Note the pair of air cushion stamps on a massive concrete base on the left. An empty engine house at Johnson's Shaft is prominent, and on the skyline to the left of its stack can be seen the headframe of Counthouse Shaft. There were two engine houses here (see Ordish, 1968, 47) but the last was demolished in the early 1980s when Redmoor became the proposed site of the South West Consolidated Tin Mine. Little survives at the gorse-covered site today. The photograph, looking north east, was used on the cover jacket of Dines, 1956, volume II.

J. Rhodes, August 1945 [A8145] SX 356710

Count House Shaft headgear, Redmoor Mine
This unusual headgear was erected when Counthouse Shaft was reopened in 1943. The shaft is inclined (note the ladder) and raised material was emptied into the hopper. The headgear on the right is over a shallow shaft to stopes with pillars containing some wolfram. Despite disappointing results with tin and wolfram, some use was made of the altered clay slate (killas), which was raised, ground to a fine powder and used as a filler for bitumenous products. Note the dump beside the truck. Looking north east.
J. Rhodes, August 1945 [A8146]   approx SX 355713

Bellan Mine at Porth Nanven

Few mines could be further west than here, where the Cot Valley reaches the coast at Porth Nanven, just south of Cape Cornwall. This is of interest as an example of a small tin mine reopened in 1942 by a shaft partway up the valley side and an adit just above high tide mark. We see the shaft, adit, mill buildings, stamps, compressed air receiver and a car. Narrow tin lodes in the granite trending parallel with the valley were worked in the past, and dumps from outcrop workings are seen on the skyline and valley sides. Bellan Mine was part of the old Bosorne and Ballowal United, working mainly at adit level and only a little below. The buildings are built of functional concrete blocks. Although since demolished, their site is still recognisable beside what is now a tarmacadamed lane. Looking north east.

J. Rhodes, August 1945 [A8081] SW 357308

Porth Nanven

A photograph taken from the same viewpoint, but looking north west. It shows how close Bellan Mine was to the water's edge, with its tramway dividing onto a double waste tip spilling onto the rocky shore. The foot of the tip must have been awash at high tide and during rough weather, so it is small wonder that most has since disappeared. This part of the photograph is a bonus as Rhodes took it to show the geological features behind - the raised beach and 'head' in the cliff, for which the cove is well known. Beyond is the granite headland of Carn Gloose which hides Cape Cornwall.

J. Rhodes, August 1945 [A8069] SW 356309

Incline in the openwork at Treveddoe Tin Mine

Also known as Old Wheal Whisper, Treveddoe is a great excavation in a stockwork about 500 feet (152 metres) long and 100 feet (30 metres) deep on the wooded east side of the Warleggan valley, 2½ miles (4 kms) west north west of St Neot. There are records of working for copper and tin since at least 1718 down to 1911, and intermittently thereafter. As the openwork became larger, the lodes were exploited by levels and shafts in the floor, the main one going down 60 fathoms (110 metres). Before and during the Second World War, developments were made underground by Liskeard Mines Co. The main openwork is far larger than this photograph of one corner indicates, despite the fact that the overgrown excavation dwarfs the 1945 incline to workings at the bottom. Looking north east.

J. Rhodes, August 1945 [A8141] SX 152696

Treveddoe water-powered stamps

The mill to dress low grade ores from Treveddoe was outside the openwork on the valley floor, where the Warleggan stream provided water as it flowed off Bodmin Moor. At the mill, a 24-foot (7.3 metres) diameter pitchback waterwheel powers a 16-head Cornish stamp battery and tables. The stamped pulp is raised by a small dipper wheel (driven from the stamps barrel) to a launder which delivers it to the two simple classifiers on the right. The spigot products pass to the tables (driven by the wheel) in the shed behind. A similar photograph was taken by Geoffrey Ordish about a year earlier (see Jenkin, 1966, 32). Looking east north east.
J. Rhodes, August 1945 [A8142] SX 151695

Round buddles working at Treveddoe
Concentrates and middlings from the tables in the shed (left) are delivered to these three convex round buddles. The nearest buddle shows the launder bringing the feed material to the top of the centre stone, the rotating arms with brushes and the overflow point on the right. The buddle in the right background is ready to be dug out. Note the crude shelters and the overhead timberwork to support the power drive shafting and gearing. The mill, rebuilt in 1943, recovered concentrates said to contain 45 per cent metallic tin. Looking east.
J. Rhodes, August 1945 [A8143] SX 151695

Sampling a buddle at Treveddoe
Elsewhere on the buddle floors, this is an instructive view showing a filled concave buddle where rings have been marked and sample cuts taken to determine the concentrate (outside ring), middlings and tailings. The three grades will be dug out separately and re-buddled as required. Note the bootprints.
J. Rhodes, August 1945 [A8144] SX 151695

68

CHAPTER NINE
OPEN OR SURFACE WORKINGS

ON OCCASIONS, THE GEOLOGY dictated that mining operations could be conducted open to the sky in the form of a quarry. There are two types of openworks illustrated here: lode-back working and stockworks. The photographs also include two 'modern' excavations, one on a lode and the other on a stockwork.

Lode-back workings were an ancient technique and the most obvious way of exploiting the back of a lode from the surface where prospectors recognised its presence by weathered 'gozzan'. Narrow open pits ('coffins' or 'goffins') were worked along the length of the lode down to a maximum of about 50 feet (15 metres) before it became too difficult to work in this way, making it necessary to resort to underground mining. Coffins might be worked back from where the lodes outcrop in sea cliffs, as seen here at Wheal Coates. These may be post-medieval workings, but primitive hammer stones and mortar stones found nearby hint at something earlier. Some lode-back workings are believed to be very ancient - perhaps even prehistoric.

Stockworks were excavated on a larger scale. A 'stockwork' contains numerous small veins of ore in a mass, and can be 60 feet (18 metres) or more wide, often in weak or altered rock. The veins are too small to be worked individually, but in a large stockwork it can be economical to excavate them all together with relative ease. The great

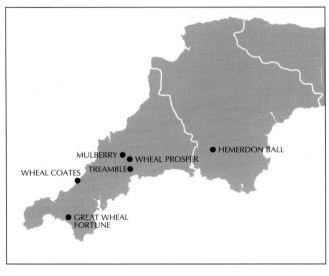

Mulberry openwork near Bodmin was described as 'one of the most ancient tin workings in Cornwall' (Collins, 1912, 72) when it was being worked along with nearby Wheal Prosper in the early twentieth century. The ore was low-grade, yielding as little as 3 lb (1.36 kg) of black tin per ton at Wheal Prosper, but it did not require hard stamping because of the large grain crystals and soft killas rock. Output was small and intermittent at these sites, but when they did work they just about paid their way if higher tin prices prevailed. In both cases the quarried ore was carried away by tramway through levels excavated from the bottom of the excavations. Mulberry had a dressing mill just to the west, where there was 'good modern machinery for crushing and dressing' in 1912. Prosper's ore was stamped and treated down in the valley to the east near Lanivet, where water-powered stamps worked during a brief revival in 1928-30 and later until 1953. They survived as a ruin until the 1980s (see Gerrard and Sharpe, 1985). Prospectors returned to the whole area in 1980-81, when diamond drilling was undertaken.

Overshadowed by copper, tin and lead mines, Cornwall and Devon also produced notable quantities of iron ore, but even the smallest price changes caused outputs of this low-value ore to vary wildly from year to year. One of the prime sources of Cornish iron ore was near Perranporth, where the Great Perran Iron Lode runs roughly south east inland for $3\frac{1}{2}$ miles (5.6 km) from Gravel Hill Mine on the coast to Deerpark Mine. It varies in width but is up to 50 feet (15 metres) or more in places. Brown haematite (limonite) lies in the upper weathered parts, with the main spathic ore (siderite) at depth. The lode was exploited mainly in the second half of the nineteenth century when its eight mines yielded at least 200,000 tons of iron ore.

Treamble Mine was worked opencast in two pits, of which Garden Quarry was about 60 feet (18 metres) deep, with levels driven from the bottom. In its working years, 1859-92, this mine produced 15,300 tons of brown haematite and a little lead and zinc ore. In 1937-40, Lloyds Perran Iron Co. opened the back of the Great Perran Iron Lode at Treamble on a large scale by means of the first heavy earth-moving equipment seen in the county (bulldozers and scrapers were photographed in action: Trounson, 1968, 11, and 1981, plates 99-100). The resulting pit was about 250 yards (228 metres) long and 150 yards (137 metres) wide. However, despite excavating 4,000 tons of ore, the lode was found to be narrower and less continuous than expected. Some underground work continued during the war, when the Home Ores Department produced 15,000 tons of ore in 1940-43.

The other 'modern' site, which also saw wartime activity, is at Hemerdon Ball in south west Devon. Here, the commercial possibility of a large wolfram-tin stockwork was recognised during the Great War and a small syndicate was set up in 1917. A new company Hemerdon Mines Ltd. erected a mill to treat 400 tons a day, but low grade ore and low prices at the end of the war brought the collapse of the firm in 1919 with losses of over £100,000. Outputs of $21\frac{1}{2}$ tons of wolfram concentrate and 6 tons of wolfram were recorded in 1918-20. The plant and equipment were sold for scrap when the firm was wound up in the mid-1930s. In 1937-8, the Hemerdon Syndicate, British (Non-Ferrous) Mining Corporation prospected the site by sinking three 60-foot (18 metres) trial shafts. In 1940, Hemerdon Wolfram Ltd., with government aid, started a second mine on a far larger scale. The new mill had a capacity of 3,000 tons a day, but it only worked for a short period and produced little wolfram. It remained on care and maintenance at the time of the photographs.

The later history of Hemerdon is significant. It was investigated again in the late 1970s by AMAX Exploration of UK Inc. and Hemerdon Mining & Smelting (UK) Ltd., when reserves of 20 million tonnes in mineralised granite were proved. There was some sampling and a pilot plant was set up. The proposed opencast mine would have excavated 2.5 million tonnes a year, making it one of the largest metal mining projects ever seen in the country. After initial delays and opposition from environmentalists, planning permission was granted in 1985, by which time falling prices had seen an end to the project.

Lode-back working at Wheal Coates

This striking photograph shows where two parallel tin lodes have been worked and the spoil dumped to the side in an area of extensive and early openworks. The country rock is metamorphosed clay slate. Looking north east, St Agnes Beacon is in the background. A survey by the Cornwall Archaeological Unit has indicated that some openworks here may be very ancient. Wheal Coates is better known for its engine house at Towanroath Shaft, perched on the cliffs above the surf near Chapel Porth near St Agnes.

J. Rhodes, August 1945 [A8123] SW 700501

Old workings at Great Wheal Fortune

Great Wheal Fortune was an ancient mine, on the east side of a valley half a mile (0.8 km) east north east of Breage near Helston. Several lodes branch into stockworks near the surface where they have been worked opencast. This photograph is believed to show the Conqueror Branches, where earlier mine workings have been exposed in a later open excavation. Minute tin-bearing cracks, nearly vertical, can be seen in the quarry face. The rock is killas and the narrow excavation measures about 400 feet (122 metres) long and 60 feet (18 metres) deep. Yields of 12 lbs (5.4 kg) of black tin per ton were reported. Looking west south west.

J. Rhodes, August 1945 [A8099] SW627288

Mulberry tin openwork

Looking south along the great Mulberry openwork, 1½ miles (2.4 km) north west of Lanivet. A tin stockwork has been opened up in a huge excavation some 900 feet (274 metres) long, 150 feet (46 metres) wide and 120 feet (36 metres) deep. Small quantities of wolfram and copper ore were also encountered here. Five men can be seen working on the face on the left. Note also the road beyond. The dressing plant, with 176 heads of stamps, was in the valley a quarter of a mile (0.4 km) west, connected by two adits, one in the floor of the pit (Jenkin, 1964, 31-36). Recorded output in 1859-1916 was 1,350 tons of tin. This old work, which was marked on Thomas Martyn's Map of Cornwall in 1748, remains an impressive overgrown gash in Mulberry Down. Two views looking north, photographs A425 and A427, were published in Dewey, 1935, Plate XB, and Dines, 1956, Plate XB.

T. C. Hall, 1.00 p.m. 5 September 1907 [A426] SX 019658

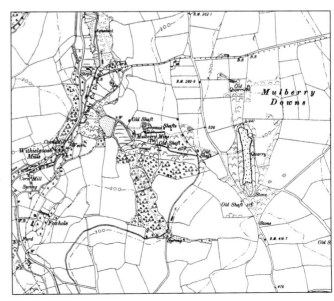

Wheal Prosper

Wheal Prosper lay just half a mile (0.8 km) west of Lanivet and differed from Mulberry as the stockwork trends east-west. The largest of four opencasts was immediately north of the old highway from Bodmin and was up to 150 feet (46 metres) deep. Note the tramway at the bottom. Wheal Prosper was worked to 1909, and again in 1928-30. The water-powered dressing mill was near a stream just north of Lanivet, to which ore was taken through an adit. An estimated 2 million tons of rock were excavated from this pit which has now been completely filled in. Looking west. One-second exposure.

T. C. Hall, 11 a.m. 5 September 1907 [A428]
SW 030642

The Great Perran Iron Lode at Treamble

The Great Perran Iron Lode was worked by eight mines along its 3½-mile (5.6 km) length, mostly underground but occasionally opencast. Beginning in 1937, Treamble Mine was the scene of an attempted reworking by Lloyd's Perran Iron Co. using the latest in heavy earth-moving machinery. This photograph, looking south east (not east north east as recorded by Rhodes), shows the result eight years later when the great pit at Treamble had been abandoned. The lode is dipping 45° south (to right). A landscape devastated by earth-movers is not a scene normally associated with Cornish metal mining.

J. Rhodes, August 1945 [A8129] SW 789558

Hemerdon Ball wolfram excavation

Hemerdon Ball lies not far from Plymouth on the edge of Dartmoor, where there is a large wolfram and tin stockwork. Wartime demands for tungsten led to prospecting and attempts to work this in an open excavation in 1917-19, and again in the Second World War when it was brought into a 'producing condition'. Looking south west, this view shows the opencast with two benches excavated in 1943-44. The small windlass on the right is above a 60-foot (18 metres) prospecting shaft. An attempt by AMAX Exploration of UK Inc. to make Hemerdon the largest wolfram opencast mine in Europe was abandoned when tungsten prices fell in the 1980s. Had it gone ahead, the planned final excavation would have been 754 feet or 230 metres deep. Published in Dines, 1956, Plate XIIIA.

J. Rhodes, August 1945 [A8150] SX 573584

Hemerdon Ball wolfram mine

A distant view, looking south south west, gives an indication of the scale of the ambitious wartime scheme at Hemerdon. It shows the great mill erected in the early 1940s to treat 3,000 tons of ore per day, the openwork on the left and the overhead ropeway (right) for taking spoil to the waste dumps. The pond in the foreground is a settling pond for a china clay works in the intervening valley.

J. Rhodes, August 1945 [A8153] SX 572587

Wolfram mill at Hemerdon Ball

The interior of the large purpose-built Hemerdon mill, seen here in pristine condition because it had only worked for about a year. Ore first passed through a primary crusher and washer. The fines from the washer were treated in the 8-spigot Stokes hydrosizer (middle floor) which supplied coarse material to jigs (below the hydrosizers) and finer material to the sand tables (bottom left). Photograph A8155 shows cone crushers, sand tables and slime treatment plant. The machinery is said to have been broken up in 1959 but the building remains ruinous.

J. Rhodes, August 1945 [A8154] SX 572587

CHAPTER TEN
STREAM-WORKING

T HERE IS HARDLY A VALLEY in Cornwall without evidence somewhere of the working over of its gravels for stream tin. The origin of these deposits lies back in geological time when the surface granite and exposed backs of the lodes were weathered out and eroded under wet tropical conditions. The more resistant tin stones remained as eluvial deposits while the rest was washed away. During periglacial conditions of the Ice Ages, weathered material was carried downslope by the process of solifluction, or by meltwaters, to end up in the valley floors as alluvial deposits which were often of a considerable depth; the heavier tin stones were concentrated among the sands and gravels. The working of these deposits for tin must date back to the Bronze Age when, unlike copper, such abundance and ease of extraction made it hardly necessary for underground mining.

The operation of *tin-streaming* to extract the cassiterite involved the directing of a flow of water in a valley floor excavation to wash away the lighter gravels and sands in order to collect the heavier tin. This was carried on, presumably in prehistoric times, and certainly in the medieval period and later (Gerrard, 1987).

On Bodmin Moor, most valleys bear the scars or marks of former tin-streaming, but they are extremely difficult to date. In August 1907, Hall took a sequence of photographs (A498-504) of the streamworks at Buttern Hill and Kenton Marsh high up

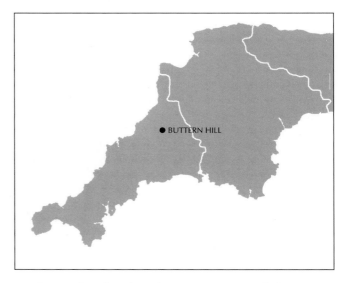

on the north side of Bodmin Moor. Four of these were published by George Barrow (1908), but photographs of streamers at work are very rare and some are therefore worth reproducing after 90 years. Their added interest is that they concern wolfram rather than tin, although working methods were the same. They were taken at a time when the stream-works were described in detail by Barrow, who recognised that 'the history of this local wolfram-working, which marks the survival of streaming, is so curious that it is worth recording'

(Barrow, 1908, 387). We can be thankful for his description and these photographs taken by his colleague to illustrate his paper.

Deposits beneath the great marsh at Bowithick had been turned over for tin by the 'Old Men' probably for centuries, but they ceased near the foot of Buttern Hill where the deposits contained too much wolfram, then considered 'a costly nuisance.' The old streamers picked out the wolfram and piled it to one side and these heaps were found when the workings were reopened in the early twentieth century, when wolfram had become greatly valued.

The hillside working was in a shallow hollow containing unsorted solifluction material about 6 feet (1.8 metres) thick in the centre and containing some large masses of wolfram. The wolfram was extracted by directing water to the top of the hollow above the workings in a leat around the edge of Buttern Hill from the head of a stream. To prevent pollution of the stream below, low step-like walls were built across the hollow so that the heavier debris and sand was washed down and deposited behind them, the sand then filtering the muddier waters. When each dam was full a new one was built (see Plate A500).

Barrow (1908, 390-1) described:

'The water from the leat is turned into a short wood-lined trough, terminating in a small waterfall with a drop of about 2 feet, a bar being placed at the lip of the fall, above the water, to regulate the flow ... Below the fall is a wooden trough, through which the finer ore settles; the finer the ore is, the longer is this trough and the lower is its slope. The whole arrangement about the waterfall is called the tie or tye, and here the tieman or tyeman stands, who treats the deposit as it is brought in wheelbarrows by the diggers and thrown under the waterfall. Armed with a pronged fork, or (in common parlance) a potato-digger, the tyeman forks over the earth and its contents, thus assisting in washing away the finer mud and sand and picking out the larger fragments that will not pass the prongs. These fragments are picked over by another man, who separates big pieces of wolfram, or vein-quartz and wolfram, the rest being thrown aside.

After a number of barrow-loads have been turned over under the fall, a heap accumulates, composed of coarse fragments and sand associated with all but the most finely-divided wolfram. This is taken out and later handed to the vanner, who vans it in small quantities at a time with a broad, slightly- concave shovel, which he dips repeatedly in a large tub of water. The cleanness and rapidity with which an expert does this is perhaps the most fascinating part of the whole process. As a certain amount of vein-quartz adheres to some of the larger pieces of wolfram, the ore from beneath the tye is crushed in a hand-mill and re-vanned, when it is ready for market. The finer ore that settles in the long wooden trough below the fall is also vanned, but needs no later treatment.

Except for the original cost of making the leat, the working expenses here are reduced to a minimum; the conditions are ideal, and the work has been steadily remunerative.'

This account describes the methods seen in the photographs at Kenton Marsh, to which attention was turned after initial success on Buttern Hill. It was the marsh from which the leat stream emerged, in ground previously turned over for tin and where wolfram had been left behind. Conditions were not so ideal here and Barrow saw the system of working as 'distinctly primitive, the field of operations covering only a small area at a time.' The streamers encountered a mass of debris (peat fragments, rough gravel and soft dirt) dumped by the previous workers and blocking the stream. All this had to be washed and sorted, involving the treatment of much barren material, but they also found pockets of tin and wolfram in the uneven floor of the marsh. A trial trench across the marsh found the peat undisturbed, with encouraging gravel beneath, but if the operation was to be successful the thick peat in the centre would have to be removed by something more efficient than shovels and wheelbarrows. Other trials were made near Fowey Well, where a new reservoir was made as far up the hill as possible, and the water brought down in canvas pipes to deliver a powerful jet to wash out the material.

Ten years after Barrow's visit, the area was being actively worked by British Tungsten Mines. There was much investment and even a floating dredger was tried behind a dam in Bowithick Marsh, below the workings on Buttern Hill. There was a dressing plant (the foundations still survive), but after investing £30,000 here, activities were suspended in early 1918 when it was claimed that most of the ore was ilmenite, a titanium mineral, and not wolfram. All the plant was sold off soon afterwards. This is a fascinating area, where all the streaming sites can be investigated, with leats and branches (all dry) around the side of Buttern Hill. The main leat emerged from a masonry dam, now breached, high up a narrow valley at the edge of Kenton Marsh.

Buttern Hill wolfram deposit

This view shows the Buttern Hill wolfram deposit, looking south west. The deposit here is being washed down a hollow in the hillside, where a series of steps have been made by building walls to form settling dams. Mineral-bearing sand settles behind a wall and when flush with the top, another wall is built. The sand filters the mud and prevents pollution of the Penpont Water downstream. The site is now difficult to recognise from this photograph, having been much enlarged in the Great War to reach further up the hill. Short adits also follow lodes found beneath the deposit. This photograph was published in Barrow, 1908, Plate XLV.

T. C. Hall, noon, 17 August 1907 [A500] SX 178822

Working the Kenton Marsh wolfram deposit
This is a new working for wolfram, previously discarded, being excavated in the Old Men's Workings in the Kenton or Nine Stones Marsh, at around 900 feet (274 metres) above sea level. The material being dug away is the old refuse of the earlier streamers who left all the wolfram and much associated stream tin. It is taken by wheelbarrows to the tie on the left. Note the planked barrow-runs and generally wet and boggy appearance of the site. Looking west south west. One-second exposure. Published in Barrow, 1908, Figure 2.
T. C. Hall, 4 p.m. 17 August 1907 [A502] SX 168821

Kenton Marsh wolfram deposit
A closer view of the deposit showing its thickness and the refuse of the earlier streamers. All the surface peat has grown since their work was abandoned. Note the wheelbarrow. Looking south west. One-second exposure.
T. C. Hall, 4.20 p.m. 17 August 1907 [A503] SX 168821

The tie at Kenton Marsh

This shows the small waterfall and escape trough, the whole called the tie. The material is dug out and carried in barrows and thrown under the fall, where it is forked over by the tieman. Fine mud, peat, etc. flows through the trough. Larger lumps of rock are taken out with the fork seen in the tieman's hand and any large bits of wolfram are picked out. The finest ore settles on the wooden trough in front. The remainder stays near the fall mixed with fine gravel. The waterfall, behind the tieman, is out of focus because the photograph required a one-second exposure on this dull day. Looking west south west.

T. C. Hall, 4.15 p.m. 17 August 1907 [A504] SX 168821

CHAPTER ELEVEN
TIN SALVAGE WORKS

TIN SALVAGE OR TIN RECOVERY works were distinct from tin-streaming (in which tin is won from the ground), although they were usually termed as such. They were found in all mining districts, where every river valley was filled with stream works of all sizes, treating and salvaging the last possible tin from the residue discharged from the mines' dressing floors above. This was never more apparent than around the Camborne-Redruth district, of which MacAlister wrote:

> At the present time an enormous quantity of black tin is annually lost to such mines as Wheal Grenville, Dolcoath, Carn Brea, East Pool, South Crofty and Wheal Basset, in the form of slime tin, the complete saving of which is a problem as yet unsolved. In the event of such solution the many stream works situated below the mines on the Red River and the river which runs down from Wheal Basset would become idle. In 1904 over £37,000 was realised by the sale of black tin extracted from the refuse of these mines by stream work companies situated on the rivers below them.'

(Hill & MacAlister, 1906, 269)

That there was still plenty to be had is well seen on the

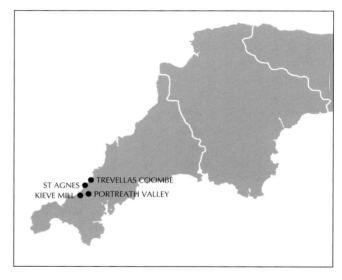

second edition Ordnance Survey six-inch scale maps (revised in 1906). The appropriately-named Red River had 21 stream works along its length of 7 miles (11.2 kms), from Newton Moor to the sea at Gwithian. Another four stream works were on the Pool tributary. In addition, the stream from Carnkie to Portreath had 13 stream works in 4½ miles (7.2 kms), and seven more on its tributary through Gilbert's Coombe below Redruth.

Kelly's Directory of Cornwall for 1906 lists the following 'tin streamers' along the Red River:

LOCATION	NAME OF STREAM WORKS	MANAGER
BREA	John Harris	
	James Rodda	
	Edward Vine	
TUCKINGMILL	Brea Tin Streaming Co.	John Whitworth
	Roscroggan Tin Streaming Co.	Richard Jackson
	Tehidy Mill Tin Stream Co.	James Jackson (sec)
	Tolvaddon Tin Stream Co.	John Whitworth
	Trevarno Tin Stream Co.	John Whitworth
	William Williams	
ROSEWARNE	Alfred Lanyon & Co.	W.C. Evans
RESKADINNICK	Reskadinnick Tin Streaming Co.	John Thomas Rule
	Kieve Mill Tin Stream	William James Edwards
KEHELLAND	Bushorn Tin Stream	Richard Evans
	Menadarva Tin Stream Co.	Edwin Kemp
	John Smith	
	South Nancemellan Tin Stream Co.	Frederick Jeffrey
POOL	Bracket Tin Stream Co.	Edward Vine
	Tregajorran Tin Streaming Co.	James Jewell
	Stephen Tresize	

A few of these can be identified on the maps. It is likely that some controlled more than one stream works (for example, John Whitworth was manager of three). Apart from a total of 37 streamers listed around the Red River and Portreath area, there were only nine others for the whole of the rest of Cornwall; of these, just one on Bodmin Moor was a tin-streamer in the true sense.

To treat the slimes the Red River valley floor was filled with round frames, long lines of ragging frames and settling pits. Indeed, these already second-hand slimes were treated several times as they passed down the valley. Thus, it was possible that some material flowing into the Kieve Mill works in these photographs could have already been through 17 other works upstream. This particular works and the sand and slimes were described by MacAlister. Before reaching the works, the Red River was divided into two by a wooden partition with sluices to control its flow into one part or the other. This allowed a

KEY
● STREAM WORKS
◆ MINE

PORTREATH AND RED RIVER STREAM WORKS

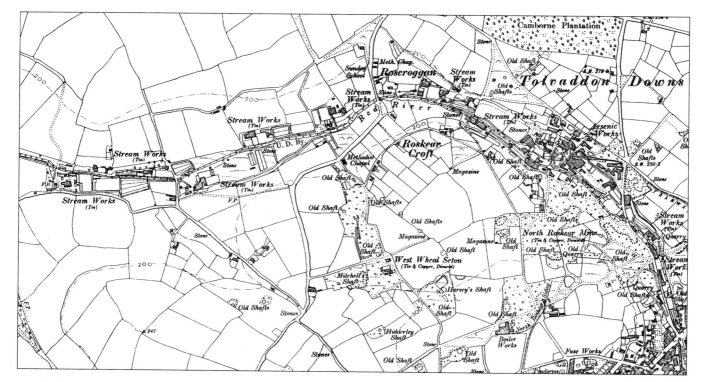

steady flow to be maintained throughout the year. Stops or partitions placed across the river just above the works trapped the coarse sand material (containing 0.75 to 1.24 per cent cassiterite), and the rest passed into long pits where the slime settled. The reddish-brown slime, which contained about 0.5 per cent cassiterite, was stirred up in a current and passed on to a large array of ragging frames. The concentrate from these was settled in pits, passed over more frames, settled again and treated on revolving tables made locally by F. Bartle & Sons. After a final buddling, the remaining concentrate was found to contain 40 per cent cassiterite, with tourmaline, much haematite and a little fluorspar.

Meanwhile, the trapped sands from above the works were washed down into strips or troughs containing wooden 'stops'

to trap the heavier material while the lighter stuff flowed over the top. This new trapped material contained about 1 per cent cassiterite and was pulverised in a rotary mill before passing to revolving frames and buddles. Despite these extensive processes, samples showed there was still about 1.5 per cent tin in sands recovered $^3/_4$ mile (1.2 km) downstream from the site (Hill & MacAlister, 1906, 273-4).

Once they were set up, the valley stream works appeared to operate unattended day and night, although the streamer was usually there or nearby. Some of the traditional stream works carried on into the 1960s, for example at Brea, Tuckingmill and Tolvaddon on the Red River and at Tolgus in the Portreath valley (for a description of Brea Adit Works, see Stoyel, 1976). Although it ceased in 1969 after 150 years of family ownership, the Tolgus Tin works became a tourist attraction while still producing tin concentrates throughout the 1970s. At that time there were more up-to-date works at Brea and Roscroggan which were treating material being excavated from old mine dumps in the district. Some modern plants, using flotation recovery methods, continued until the tin crisis of 1985. At the time of writing, Tolgus Tin is being revitalised by the Trevithick Trust as a working site with equipment including a 12-head stamps, round frames, Holman tables and slime pits.

The St Agnes and St Just mining areas were also notable for tin salvage stream works, and the former district is recorded here in the first two photographs.

Tin salvage works at Trevellas Coombe, St Agnes
This is among the earliest photographs in the BGS collection. Although a bit hazy, it is an excellent example of a typical Cornish coombe or valley containing tin salvage works. In this case, the tin is being recovered from slimes brought down in the stream from the Jericho Stamps of West Wheal Kitty at the head of the valley. Ragging frames and round frames are evident in the foreground, with a second works beyond; a third works is hidden around the distant corner of the coombe just below the dressing floors at Jericho Stamps. The tradition continues today in this fascinating valley. Not far from this site the Blue Hills Tin Streams has a working water stamps, dressing floors and even small-scale tin smelting which can be seen on guided tours.
J. B. Scrivenor, June 1903 [A94] SW 729515

St Agnes Tin Salvage Works

Another early photograph in the collection. At the bottom of Trevaunance Coombe, this view shows the last possible site for a tin salvage works before the washings brought down from Wheal Kitty's stamps end up on the beach of Trevaunance Cove. Sand on the beach was also worked for the traces of tin which had still escaped. Note the pond (left), ragging frames, round frames and waterwheels. The long building is a hammer mill, since demolished.

The site is hardly recognisable today, as it is now a car park. The photograph also provides a good view of the interesting little harbour which served the mines and local community for many years. Storms destroyed the piers between 1915 and 1924, leaving only their granite foundations exposed at low tide. The sea is deceptively calm, for this was a dangerous coast for shipping.

J. B. Scrivenor, June 1903 [A95] SW 721515

Slime pits at the Kieve Mill Tin Stream Works, Reskadinnick
MacAlister described these long pits for collecting slime at the start of the tin recovery stages at this stream works on the Red River. The controlling sluices are in the foreground, but the rest of the works is mostly hidden at a lower level in the valley beyond. Published in Hill & MacAlister, 1906, plate XXI.
D. A. MacAlister & T. C. Hall, 3.30 p.m. 18 September 1904 [A55] SW 635420

Ragging frames at Kieve Mill
Long lines of self-acting rack, rag or ragging frames, taken from the far end of the slime pits. There are more beyond the waterwheels. Slimes are fed onto the flat surface of the rag frame, where the heavier particles collect, to be washed off into a launder at intervals. Photograph A57 shows the tin yard with masses of overhead launders and two waterwheels. At the time of the photograph, the Kieve Mill Tin Stream was managed by William James Edwards. It was a large works and, for example, the reported sale of 87 tons of black tin some years later in 1920 indicates how much material must have been flowing down the Red River. Looking north west. Published in Hill & MacAlister,1906, plate XXIV.
D. A. MacAlister & T. C. Hall, 3.15 p.m. 18 September 1904 [A56] SW 634420

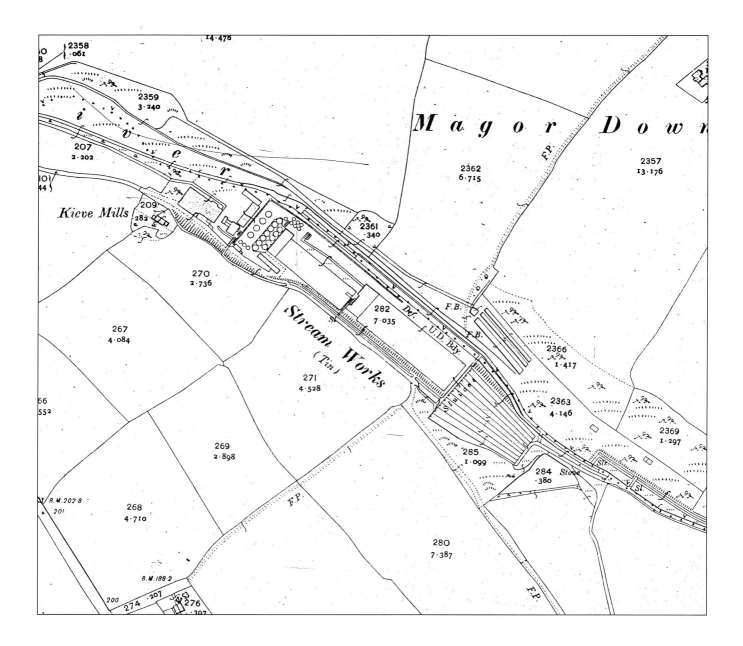

Tin stream works and calciner in the Portreath Valley

One of many small stream works erected down the valley from Redruth, recovering small amounts of tin from the waste from the dressing plants of mines above. Although the recovery was small, such a stream works was cheap to operate by water power (on the right) and was largely self-operating. The distinctive square structure with a pyramid roof is a calciner for treating sulphides; its flue leads to the chimney stack up the hill. Today, the site has been filled and levelled but the calciner survives as the last complete example with machinery (pictured on the right). It is said to have been erected second-hand as recently as 1933, and is described by Sharpe (1991, 156-9). The milestone ('REDRUTH TC 1 MILE PORTREATH 3 MILES') is still there beside the B3300 road. The Tolgus Tin works is a short distance downstream.

J. Rhodes, August 1945 [A8117] SW 690431

IN 1945, MINING WAS recorded taking place for three very different minerals in and around the lower Teign valley. Two were hard-rock mines, for barytes and micaceous haematite; the others were for softer ball clay in the Bovey Basin. A triangle of high ground on the north-eastern edge of the Dartmoor National Park, bounded by the converging Bovey and Teign valleys, was the scene of mining in the nineteenth and twentieth centuries. The lead mines of the Teign valley are better known, but the two mines illustrated here were for the more unusual minerals of barytes and micaceous haematite. Bridford and Great Rock Mines were both in remote, rural settings off the Teign valley.

Although the presence of barytes (heavy spar) had been known in and around the lead mines of the Teign valley since the early nineteenth century, it was not until after about 1870 that wider markets became available. The chemical industry was expanding and barytes, which was already used as a filler in paper, was now added to paint pigments. The barytes mine at Bridford saw a long period of production, from 1875 to 1958. The first phase from 1875 to 1927 was mostly open-cast working down to about 90 feet (27 metres) and average annual output was less than 1,500 tons. In 1927, the Devon Baryta Co. was bought out by Malehurst Barytes Co. Ltd., who already had interests in Shropshire. Their new manager, Lt-Col. J. V. Ramsden, set about modernising the plant and developing

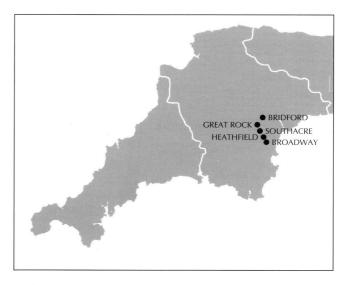

underground mining in a most efficient manner. Annual production rose dramatically to over 10,500 tons. The partly processed barytes ore had been carried to a grinding mill at Exeter, but now that was abandoned in favour of a modern crushing and concentration plant installed on the mine site. About 50 per cent of the ore was recovered in jigs and 35 per cent on tables, but the rest was lost as slimes. Importantly, the Malehurst Co. also paid attention to marketing and began developing links with Bernard Laporte & Co., paint and chemical manufacturers of Luton. In 1950 the firm became a total subsidiary of the Laporte Group and the mine was worked in its final years under the name of Laporte Minerals Ltd.

New Shaft was begun on the north-south No.1 Vein at the end of 1929, and had reached 280 feet (85 metres) by 1937 when there were four levels opening up new veins, of which the most important was No.4. There were nearly 6 miles (9.6 km) of underground levels by 1943. Despite the usual wartime shortages of materials and labour, Bridford Mine produced 12,500 tons of barytes in 1945 at the time of the photographs. Five years later, the deepest workings were down to 380 feet (116 metres). New Shaft was down to 600 feet (183 metres) by 1952, working on Nos.1 and 4 Veins, but this main shaft was becoming increasingly unsafe and there were falls underground. Reserves of barytes were becoming exhausted, it was said, so the mine was closed in July 1958 and 40 workers became unemployed (see Schmitz, 1977).

A short distance to the south, in an even more isolated, wooded location lay the Great Rock Mine, which was the largest of the micaceous haematite mines and the last of any mine to work on Dartmoor. After being dressed to a high concentrate, this soft and friable 'shiny ore' was used in the manufacture of anti-corrosive paints for iron and steel structures.

Details are less clear of mining at 'Hennock' since the 1820s, but in its last working a mine at Great Rock was re-opened by Otto Schmidt & Co. in 1896. Six years later, the Great Rock Mine came to the Ferrubron Manufacturing Co. who worked it down to its closure in 1969. Ferrubron also obtained other local micaceous haematite mines, at Hawkmoor, Shaptor and Shuttamoor in 1902, with Plumbley and Kelly added later. However, only Great Rock and Kelly remained at work by the Great War.

Great Rock Mine worked groups of east-west lodes centred around the South, North and Beadon Lodes on both sides of a hill by means of 17 adits and six shafts. Output, with Kelly Mine included, was about 400 tons a year. The raised ore was crushed, washed and carried off in water through launders by which it became graded because of the shape of the grains. The dressing mill was linked to drying sheds 550 yards (500 metres) away in Hyner Bottom by a wooden launder which carried the concentrate suspended in water. Great Rock was closed in 1969 and the surface equipment removed two years later.

The nearby Kelly Mine, which may date back to the 1790s, was re-opened by the Scottish Silvoid Co. in 1900 and taken over by Ferrubron in 1917. It was always a small mine but continued until 1946. It remains of interest because its surface equipment, which includes a small set of Californian stamps, has survived and is being conserved by the Kelly Mine Preservation Society. Great Rock and Kelly Mine are described in Atkinson, Burt and Waite, 1978, and Roberts, 1996.

In total contrast are the ball clays of the Bovey Basin. The Bovey Beds are Oligocene sediments derived from Dartmoor and deposited in a deep basin, to include clays, sands, gravels and lignites. Among the beds are the dark Potting Clays, exported for high quality white earthenware, below which are the lighter coloured Stoneware Clays, siliceous clays used locally for drain pipes, tiles and bricks. These deposits have been worked commercially in the area between Chudleigh Knighton, Kingsteignton and Newton Abbot since the first half of the eighteenth century. The ball clay was carried on the Stover and Hackney Canals and down the Teign estuary for export from Teignmouth, but today this traffic is taken by road to the docks.

By the twentieth century, there were three methods of working the ball clays. The thicker beds of the stoneware clays were usually worked in opencut quarries or large square pits. The potters clays, being thinner and steeply dipping, were worked by square pits on their outcrops, but more often underground from shafts and drives. The clay was cut out with 'tubills' in square blocks or balls.

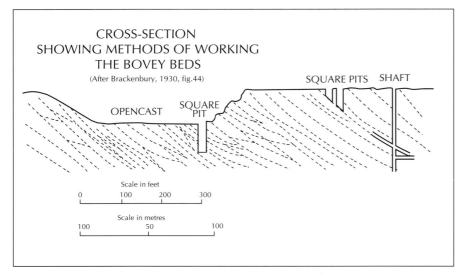

CROSS-SECTION
SHOWING METHODS OF WORKING
THE BOVEY BEDS
(After Brackenbury, 1930, fig.44)

off-shoots. The pumping and hoisting engine houses were erected some distance from the shaft because the ground was liable to subsidence during mining. A fixed engine might work four or more shafts, which were themselves being relocated as areas were worked out. Power was transmitted by wire ropes supported on iron pulley-wheels on wooden posts, a light-weight system which could be re-arranged as the ground shifted or new shafts were opened. Hoisting was by wire ropes. Clay was raised in the shafts and square pits in a rectangular bucket holding about $4\frac{1}{2}$ cwt (228 kg). Pumping was by Cornish bucket-pumps, worked by an angle bob and wire rope from gearing connected to an electric motor.

The square pits were about 20 feet (6 metres) square and held open in the soft ground by strong timber stays. They might be 100 feet (30 metres) deep. Shafts were sunk to 150 feet (45 metres) from which the beds could be worked. By the fan method, beds with an inclination of 35° were worked from two levels driven in opposite directions and then a series of converging drives. For thicker and less steeply inclined beds, the clay was exploited by main drives, secondary drives and

Today, almost all the ball clay is excavated from large open pits, although there are three drift mines working deeper deposits. There were once several small firms involved, but now Watts, Blake, Bearne & Co. Plc and ECC Ball Clays control the industry. An outline history of the industry has been given by Rolt (1974).

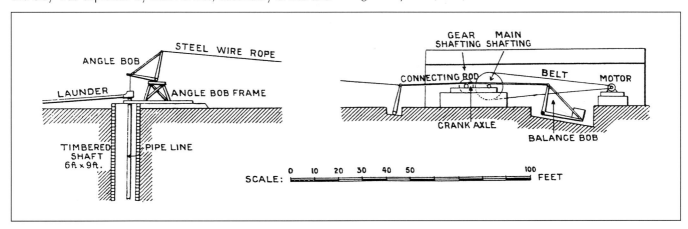

New Shaft headgear at Bridford Barytes Mine
The timber headframe above New Shaft, which was sunk from 1929 onwards. Ore is raised in skips, crushed and carried on the conveyor belt to the mill (left). Dressing tables and washing plant are in the building behind. A photograph (A8165) underground at the 380-foot level of this mine can be seen in Chapter Four. The rural setting is evident in this view which looks south east towards the Teign valley. Published in Dines, 1956, Plate XVA.
J. Rhodes, August 1945 [A8167] SX 830865

Sizing plant and conveyors at Bridford Mine

This is the plant to which the conveyor brings the mined ore. At the top are revolving screens for sizing the ore, the oversize being recrushed in rolls (on lower stage) and returned to the circuit by the shorter conveyor belt rising on the left. Coarser size passing through the screens (over $\frac{1}{2}$inch or 13 mm) is treated in jigs, and the fines are further subdivided by Stokes hydrosizers (on lower stage) into three grades which are fed to dressing tables in the mill. Note the camouflage paint on the corrugated iron building. In the background is the old opencast on No.1 Vein. Looking north. A sketch of the surface layout of the mine in c.1940 by J. V. Ramsden, manager, is given in Schmitz, 1977, 119.

J. Rhodes, August 1945 [A8169] SX 830865

Sizing plant at Bridford Mine
A closer view of the massive timber construction of the sizing plant, looking back towards New Shaft. Other photographs in the collection, A8171-4, are rather poor but show the mill, dressing tables and delivery to lorries.
J. Rhodes, August 1945 [A8170] SX 830865

Great Rock Mine

A general view of the Great Rock micaceous haematite mine, almost hidden among the trees on a steep valley slope where it is worked from adits. There is a side-tipping tram wagon above the mill on the left. The mine office is in the small bungalow in front of which is a growing waste tip. Four women workers (due to wartime labour shortages?) are standing among the tailings. A useful contemporary account of the mine operation was written by Michell (1945). A photograph (A8157) underground in Beadon Adit is in Chapter Four. More photographs and a description are given in Atkinson, Burt & Waite, 1978, 24-30.

J. Rhodes, August 1945 [A8158] SX 827815

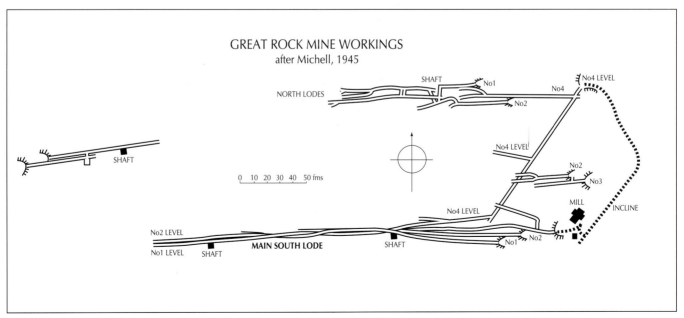

GREAT ROCK MINE WORKINGS
after Michell, 1945

The mill at Great Rock Mine

The micaceous haematite ore is crushed to about 1-inch (25 mm) size and passed in a stream of water through tubs and sluices. By virtue of its fine grain shape the ore is carried off in the stream to settling tanks. This picture shows the rotating sizing trommel (top) and feed to the tub and sluice (left foreground). Coarse material settling in the tub is being removed by the woman and dumped in the centre for regrinding in a small ball mill (feed on right background). The settlements in the sluice go to the waste dump.

J. Rhodes, August 1945 [A8159] SX 827815

Broadway Pit

A crane or 'crab' with a fixed jib above Broadway Pit. A bucket of clay has been raised by a wire from an engine some distance away (to right). The jib cannot be raised and the hand winch on the crane is for swinging it through 45° so the bucket can be tipped into the waiting truck. This in turn will be hauled up the incline for tipping onto the stockpile behind. Note the mass of timber around the shaft. The shaft has two compartments, one for the ladder way and pump rods and the other for hoisting. On the left is the balance bob for the pump in the shaft, worked by a wire. The pumped water flows out through the wooden launder to the left. The bed or seam of clay being worked is 90 feet (27 metres) below. Looking north west. Broadway later became opencast, although at the time of writing (1998) a newer drift mine is working a deeper deposit beneath. Worked by Hexter & Budge at the time of the photograph, the pit is now owned by ECC Ball Clays.

J. Rhodes, August 1945 [A8183] approx SX 861737

Tramway ramps and stockpiles at Broadway Pit

The self-tipping truck is being hauled by a wire rope from a position beyond the sheds. The clay is stockpiled in the open for weathering. Note the wires and pulleys on timber posts in the foreground, transmitting power from a central point, such an arrangement being necessary where the ground is liable to move. Looking west.

J. Rhodes, August 1945 [A8184] approx SX 861737

Southacre Pit

An open pit, showing the nature of the beds and the method of working in benches. The clay deposit is being dug by hand on the right. When filled, the side-tipping wagon is pushed a short distance to tip down the chute into a truck which climbs out of the pit onto the stockpile or waste tip. An earlier incline can be seen in the background. The photograph clearly shows the different grades of inclined clays, sands and probably lignite. As in 1945, Southacre is still owned by Watts, Blake, Bearne & Co. and has become the largest pit in the Bovey Basin.

J. Rhodes, August 1945 [A8178] approx SX 855755

Pipe making at Heathfield
The end product of some of the Bovey Beds. This is at the Great Western Potteries (Candy & Co.). On the floor above clay is fed into a pipe press on the left and moulded under pressure. A pipe is seen emerging on the left. It is then put vertically on a wooden slab on a revolving table where it is trimmed and grooves are made at both ends with a comb. The pipes are stacked for drying before they are fired.
J. Rhodes, August 1945 [A8186]   approx SX 834761

BIBLIOGRAPHY

Atkinson, M., Burt, R. and Waite, P. (1978) *Dartmoor Mines: The Mines of the Granite Mass*, Exeter IA Group

Barrow, G. (1908) 'The High-level Platforms of Bodmin Moor and their relation to the deposits of stream-tin and wolfram', *Quart. Jnl. Geol. Soc.*, 64, 384-400

Barton, D. B. (1967a) *A History of Tin Mining and Smelting in Cornwall*, Bradford Barton

Barton, D. B. (1967b) *Historic Cornish Mining Scenes Underground*, Bradford Barton

Barton, D. B. (1968) *A History of Copper Mining in Cornwall & Devon,* Bradford Barton

Barton, D. B. (1969) *The Cornish Beam Engine*, Bradford Barton

Brackenbury, C. (1930) 'Clay Mining in South Devon', *Trans. Inst. Mining & Metallurgy*, XL, 238-277

Bristow, C. M. (1996) *Cornwall's Geology and Scenery*, Cornish Hillside Publications

Buckley, J. A. (1989) *Geevor Mine*, Geevor Tourist Amenity

Buckley, J. A. (1997) *History of South Crofty Mine*, Dyllansow Truran

Burrow, J. C. (1894) 'Photography in Mines', *Trans. Roy. Geol. Soc. Cornwall*, XI, 621-633

Burrow, J. C. and Thomas, W. (1893) *'Mongst Mines and Miners: or Underground Scenes by Flash-light,* London and Camborne (reprinted Bradford Barton, 1965)

Collins, J. H. (1912) 'Observations on the West of England Mining Region', *Trans. Roy. Geol. Soc.* Cornwall, XIV

De La Beche, H. T. (1839) *Report on the Geology of Cornwall, Devon and West Somerset,* Memoir

Dewey, H. (1935) *British Regional Geology: South-West England*, HMSO (and 2nd edition, 1948)

Dewey, H. and Dines, H. G. (1923) *Tungsten and Manganese Ores, Mem. Geol. Survey, Mineral Resources*, vol 1, 3rd edition

Dines, H. G. (1956) *The Metalliferous Mining Region of South West England*, 2 volumes, HMSO

Earl, B. (1978) *Cornish Explosives*, Trevithick Society

Earl, B. (1994) *Cornish Mining*, Cornish Hillside Publications

Embrey, P. G. and Symes, R. F. (1987) *Minerals of Cornwall and Devon*, British Museum (Natural History)

Fawns, S. (1912) *Tin Deposits of the World*, The Mining Journal, 3rd edition

Gerrard, S. (1987) 'Streamworking in medieval Cornwall', *Journal of the Trevithick Society*, No.14, 7-31

Gerrard, S. and Sharpe, A. (1985) 'Archaeological Survey and Excavation at Wheal Prosper Tin Stamps, Lanivet', *Cornish Archaeology*, No.24, 196-211

Harris, T. R. (1974) *Dolcoath: Queen of Cornish Mines*, Trevithick Society

Hill, J. B. and MacAlister, D. A. (1906) *Geology of Falmouth and Truro and of the Mining District of Camborne and Redruth*, Memoir for sheet 352, Geological Survey

Jenkin, A. K. H. (1948) *The Cornish Miner*, Allen & Unwin, 1927, 2nd edition

Jenkin, A. K. H. (1964) *Mines and Miners of Cornwall, IX. Padstow, St Columb and Bodmin*, Truro Bookshop

Jenkin, A. K. H. (1965) *Mines and Miners of Cornwall, X. Camborne-Illogan*, Truro Bookshop

Jenkin, A. K. H. (1966) *Mines and Miners of Cornwall, XII. Around Liskeard*, Truro Bookshop

Michell, F. B. (1945) 'Mineral Pigments', *Mine and Quarry Engineering*, January, 9-14

Michell, F. B. (1978) 'Ore Dressing in Cornwall 1600-1900', *Journal of the Trevithick Society*, No.6, 25-52

Noall, C. (1983) *Geevor*, Geevor Tin Mines plc, Pendeen

Ordish, H. G. (1967) *Cornish Engine-Houses: A Pictorial Survey*, Bradford Barton

Ordish, H. G. (1968) *Cornish Engine-Houses: A Second Pictorial Survey*, Bradford Barton

Polkinghorne, J. R. R. (1945) 'Slate Mining - Redmoor Mine, Kelly Bray, Callington - Counthouse Section', *Trans. Roy. Geol. Soc. Cornwall*, XVII, pt 5, 269-71

Reid, C. and Flett, J. S. (1907) *Geology of the Land's End*, Memoir for sheets 351 and 358, Geological Survey

Reid, C. and Scrivenor, J. B. (1906) *Geology of the Country near Newquay*, Memoir for sheet 346, Geological Survey

Roberts, P. (1996) 'Kelly Mine: The First Ten Years', in Newman, P.(ed) *The Archaeology of Mining and Metallurgy in South-West Britain*, Peak District Mines Hist. Soc. and Historical Metallurgy Soc., 163-7

Rolt, L. T. C. (1974) *The Potters Field*, David & Charles

Schmitz, C. J. (1977) 'The Development and Decline of the Devon Barytes Industry, 1875-1958', *Rep. Trans. Devon. Ass. Advmt. Sci.*, 109, 117-133

Sevier, W. E. (1945) 'Progress at Geevor Tin Mine', *The Mining Magazine*, October, 201-210

Sharpe, A., ed. (1991) *Engine House Assessment: Mineral Tramways Project*, Cornwall Archaeological Unit

Stanier, P. (1988) *Cornwall's Mining Heritage*, Twelveheads Press

Stanier, P. (1995) *Quarries of England and Wales: an historic photographic record*, Twelveheads Press

Stoyel, A. (1976) 'Brea Adit Works, Camborne', *Journal of the Trevithick Society*, No.4, 45-56

Thomas, C. (1988) *Views and Likenesses*, Royal Institution of Cornwall

Trounson, J. H. (1968) *Historic Cornish Mining Scenes at Surface*, Bradford Barton

Trounson, J. H. (1980) *Mining in Cornwall, 1850-1960, Volume One*, Moorland Publishing

Trounson, J. H. (1981) *Mining in Cornwall, 1850-1960, Volume Two*, Moorland Publishing, 1981

Trounson, J. H. (1989) *The Cornish Mineral Industry: Past Performance and Future Prospect, a personal view 1937-1951*, University of Exeter

Watton, W. J. (1990) 'The History of Underground Photography in Cornwall', *Journal of the Trevithick Society*, No.17, 2-22

ACKNOWLEDGEMENTS

This book would not have come to fruition without the help of a number of people and organisations, all who have been most forthcoming with information when requested. In particular, Michael Messenger and Alan Kittridge, as ever, have been more than encouraging. Tony Brooks devoted much time to a discussion of Geevor and other Cornish sites, and I have also received help from Tony Cross, Bryan Earl, John Ferguson and Andrew Trenoweth. I am also grateful to the staff at the British Geological Survey, Keyworth, especially Graham McKenna, Librarian, Tim Cullen, Photographer, and Dr Jean Alexander, Copyright Manager, as well as Martin Pulsford, former Chief Photographer. The staff at the Cornish Studies Library, Redruth, and Messrs ECC Ball Clays and Watts, Blake, Bearne & Co. Plc. are also owed my thanks.

The historic photographs are reproduced by permission of the Director, British Geological Survey: NERC copyright reserved. The photograph on page 16 is from the collection of the Cornish Studies Library, and the modern photograph on page 37 is by Michael Messenger. All others are by the author.

The map extracts are reproduced by permission of the Ordnance Survey: Crown copyright reserved.

INDEX